Designing Microcomputer Systems

The Hayden Microcomputer Series

CONSUMER'S GUIDE TO PERSONAL COMPUTING AND MICROCOMPUTERS*
Stephen J. Freiberger and Paul Chew, Jr.

THE FIRST BOOK OF KIM†
Jim Butterfield, Stan Ockers, and Eric Rehnke

GAME PLAYING WITH BASIC
Donald D. Spencer

STIMULATING SIMULATIONS
C. W. Engel

SMALL COMPUTER SYSTEMS HANDBOOK†
Sol Libes

HOW TO BUILD A COMPUTER-CONTROLLED ROBOT†
Tod Loofbourrow

HOW TO PROFIT FROM YOUR PERSONAL COMPUTER*
Ted Lewis

THE MIND APPLIANCE: HOME COMPUTER APPLICATIONS*
Ted Lewis

THE 6800 MICROPROCESSOR: A SELF-STUDY COURSE WITH APPLICATIONS*
Lance A. Leventhal

THE FIRST BOOK OF MICROCOMPUTERS
Robert Moody

MICROCOMPUTERS AND THE 3 R's: A Guide for Teachers*
Christine Doerr

DESIGNING MICROCOMPUTER SYSTEMS*
Udo W. Pooch and Rahul Chattergy

Consulting Editor: Ted Lewis, Oregon State University

†*Consulting Editor: Sol Libes, Amateur Computer Group of New Jersey and Union Technical Institute*

Designing Microcomputer Systems

Udo W. Pooch
Texas A&M University

Rahul Chattergy
University of Hawaii

HAYDEN BOOK COMPANY, INC.
Rochelle Park, New Jersey

To our parents, to whom we owe everything

ISBN 0-8104-5679-6
Library of Congress Catalog Card Number 79-88618

Printed in the United States of America

1	2	3	4	5	6	7	8	9	PRINTING
79	80	81	82	83	84	85	86	87	YEAR

Preface

The purpose of this text is to provide the electronics engineer and the hobbyist with the background information necessary to build microcomputer systems. Microprocessors, which are at the heart of all microcomputer systems, are a remarkable new tool for the designer of electronic products. Not only can they lower the cost and increase the flexibility of electronic systems, they are also small and inexpensive. In the past, the application of microprocessors was limited to point-of-sale terminals. Because of their versatility, they are now used in such diverse applications as (1) traffic control systems, (2) small accounting equipment, (3) intelligent terminals for computers, (4) industrial process controllers, (5) radars, (6) sonars, (7) telephone systems, (8) display terminals, (9) test equipment, (10) video games, (11) household appliances, and so on. The range of their applications seems to be limited only by the designer's imagination.

In conjunction with memory units and peripheral devices, a microprocessor can be used to design a microcomputer. In system complexity, they are halfway between hand-held calculators and minicomputers. They are compact and inexpensive like calculators; they are also programmable like minicomputers. No wonder that mastery of the microprocessor is the most exciting challenge facing the electronic hobbyist today.

The major objective of this text is to discuss the hardware aspects of microcomputer systems. The first chapter provides the reader with an overview of microcomputer systems. It introduces him to some of the basic components of a digital computer, important attributes of microcomputers, and several popular microcomputer families. Although this book is not concerned with software, Chap. 1 emphasizes the importance of software and discusses, in general terms, software development systems for microcomputers.

Chapter 2 contains a discussion of the general features of the hardware components of a microcomputer system in detail. This includes an investigation of microprocessor architecture, input and output ports, interrupt systems, programmable clocks, memory units, and so forth. Timing diagrams are provided to explain sequences of operations in detail.

Three of the most popular microcomputer families, Intel 8080, Zilog Z-80, and Motorola 6800 are described in Chaps. 3, 4, and 5. Each system is discussed in terms of the architecture of its microprocessor, timing, control and clock signals, interrupt handling, input/output ports, and the like. Addressing schemes and instruction sets are not considered here since they properly belong in the realm of microcomputer programming. Chapter 6 is concerned with the design of interfaces for microcomputer peripheral devices. Trade-offs between software and hardware interfaces, conventional and memory-mapped input/output techniques are discussed as are design considerations for interfaces for signal converters, keyboards, printers, cassettes, floppy disks, and video and graphic displays.

Building microcomputer systems from kits and selecting the right microcomputer family for a given application are discussed in Chap. 7. It should be noted that this is not a handbook that can replace the detailed instruction sheets attached to the kits themselves. Neither does it aim to teach basic technical skills for assembling electronic kits. The objective is to present the basic concepts of microcomputer system design from the viewpoint of LSI chip sets.

UDO W. POOCH
RAHUL CHATTERGY

Contents

Chapter 1

Overview of Microcomputer Systems

Introduction

Due to advances in the technology of Large Scale Integration (LSI) of electronic circuits, microcomputer systems are finding a wide range of applications. As a tool, such systems exceed the versatility and power of all other electronic systems available. Understanding their operations is one of the most exciting challenges facing the hobbyist as well as the electronics engineer today. Microcomputers are by no means simple to understand, but their impact on daily life is so far-reaching that the effort is well worth the trouble. The study of their operations is further complicated by the dynamic nature of their development. New processors and components are developed every year, requiring a continuous updating of knowledge. The only way to function in such a rapidly growing environment is to acquire certain basic skills. Although the techniques of implementation change, the fundamental concepts remain the same. The person who masters these basics will find that there is nothing mysterious about microcomputer engineering; anyone competent in building electronic kits can not only assemble but also make profitable use of microcomputers. The purpose of this chapter is to provide the reader with an overview of microcomputer systems. Detailed discussion of specific processors, hardware, and interfacing techniques will be discussed in subsequent chapters.

Attributes of Microcomputers

There are several reasons for the popularity of microcomputers. They provide inexpensive but powerful capabilities for digital computa-

1

tion and can therefore be used in various control and information processing applications. They allow the number of components and the complexity of digital electronic systems to be greatly reduced. They also reduce turnaround design time because of their flexible and modifiable program control. Although they are complex devices, they can be easily specialized for specific applications by proper programming. In large quantities their cost is insignificant, especially in comparison to the significant value they add to the products that use them. Last but not least, they have radically simplified the process of designing digital electronic systems.

A microcomputer is controlled by instructions stored in its memory, a sequence of such instructions being called a *program*. In order to design a microcomputer system for a given application, the designer uses such programming aids as editors, assemblers, compilers, and so forth. Major design changes can sometimes be made simply by altering the stored program. A microcomputer builder, therefore, must not only know about the necessary hardware, but about programming methods and aids as well. The following sections describe some of the basic concepts involved in the understanding and use of digital computing systems.

Digital Computing Systems

A digital computer is a device for processing information by means of programs stored in its memory. A functional diagram of the digital computer is shown in Fig. 1.1. The *memory unit* (MU) stores the programs used to control the operations of the *processing unit* (PU). The information to be processed is often stored in the MU along with the program. However, in real-time data processing applications, the computer may gather this information from its environment by means of special sensors. The *input unit* (IU) is used to store programs and data in the MU. The results of computations are obtained from the PU or the MU by means of the *output unit* (OU). The PU is capable of carrying out

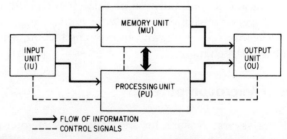

Fig. 1.1   Functional diagram of a digital computer (solid lines indicate flow of information; broken lines indicate control signals)

many different operations, such as the arithmetic operations, logic operations, character manipulations, and so forth, on the input data. The structure and the essential components of each unit are described in the following sections.

Memory Unit

In a digital computer, the memory unit stores information in the form of strings of binary digits (*bits*), for example, 0011010011. The most commonly used unit of storage is called a *memory word.* Each word has a unique *address,* which allows it to be selected from among all the words in a MU. Thus, memory can be thought of as a string of words, arranged in order of numerically increasing addresses and each composed of a string of bits (see Fig. 1.2).

WORD ADDRESS   MEMORY

0

1

2   ◄── WORD # 2

3

Fib. 1.2 Memory as a linearly ordered arrangement of words (each word can store a string of bits such as the one shown)

The process of obtaining information from a MU is called a *memory read.* The address of the word containing the needed information is put in the *memory address register* (MAR), as shown in Fig. 1.3, and a memory-read signal is applied to the MU. The address is internally decoded by the MU, and the contents of the addressed word are retrieved and put in the *memory data register* (MDR). The process of storing in-

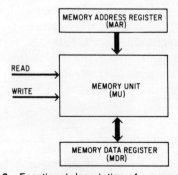

Fig. 1.3 Functional description of a memory unit

formation in a word of MU is called a *memory write*. The address of the word to be written into is put in the MAR, and the data to be written is put in the MDR. When a write signal is applied to the MU, the latter proceeds to transfer the contents of the MDR to the addressed word.

Processing Unit

The processing unit carries out all necessary operations on data obtained from the MU according to instructions also obtained from the MU. The basic data manipulation and transformation operations are carried out by an *arithmetic/logic unit* (ALU), shown in Fig. 1.4. The operation of obtaining an instruction from the MU is called an *instruction fetch*. After an instruction is fetched from the MU, it is stored in an internal register of the PU called an *instruction register* (IR). The contents of the IR are then decoded to determine the type of operation involved and the location of the data in the MU that is to be used in the operation.

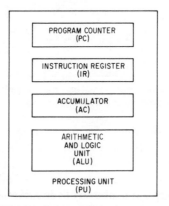

Fig. 1.4   Functional description of a processing unit

The process of obtaining data from the MU so that it can be operated on is called an *operand fetch*. The operand fetched from the MU is stored in an internal register of the PU called an *accumulator* (AC). After the completion of an operand fetch, the PU executes the decoded instruction obtained during the previous instruction fetch. This sequence of operations carried out by the PU is shown in Fig. 1.5. The address of the

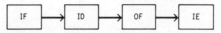

Fig. 1.5   Operating sequence of a PU (IF: Instruction Fetch; ID: Instruction Decode; OF: Operand Fetch; IE: Instruction Execution)

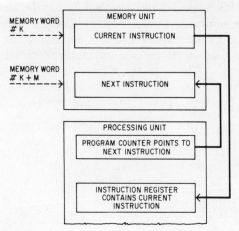

Fig. 1.6 Uses of the program counter (PC) and instruction register (IR)

word in the MU containing the next instruction to be executed by the PU is stored in an internal register of the PU called a *program counter* (PC). After the completion of the instruction decode operation, the contents of the PC are incremented by a suitable constant to point to the next instruction to be executed (see Fig. 1.6). A PU has many more internal registers for storing intermediate results, addresses, and so forth. Only the most important ones have been mentioned here. The input/output units and their interfaces to a digital computer are perhaps the most variable system components of a digital computer. These are discussed in detail in a later chapter on interfacing.

Microprocessor Families

A *microprocessor* is the processing unit of a microcomputer system. These units, built by means of LSI circuit technology, are contained in small packages called *chips* (see Fig. 1.7). The processing capabilities and the internal chip architectures of microprocessors vary over a wide spectrum. The most popular microprocessors handle data in units of *eight-bit bytes.* These include Intel's 8080 family, Motorola's 6800 fami-

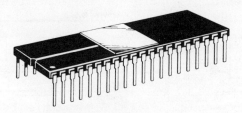

Fig. 1.7 An MC6800 microprocessor in a dual in-line package

ly, Rockwell's PPS-8 family, and Zilog's Z-80 family, among others. The 8080 system has found a wide range of applications in industrial process control, games, intelligent data terminals, and so on. The 6800 system is most commonly used in data-communication terminals, industrial instrumentation, and the like. All these processors and systems are manufactured by various other manufacturers (second sources) such as Advanced Micro Devices, Texas Instruments, NEC Microcomputers, Siemens (System 8080), American Microsystems (System 6800), and National Semiconductor (System PPS-8).

The usefulness of eight-bit microprocessors derives from their design, which concentrates most of their computing capabilities on a single processor chip. This chip not only processes data but also handles all communications and command and control functions with the help of support chips that provide information storage and input/output interfaces. The use of sixteen address lines allows Intel 8080A, Motorola 6800D, and Zilog Z-80 microprocessors to address 65,536 words of memory directly. Since most microcomputer systems do not require such large portions of directly addressable memory, the leftover addresses can be used to communicate with a large variety of input/output devices via commercially available interface chips.

The 8080A processor requires three power supplies of +5 V, −5 V, and 12 V. It has a powerful instruction set and interrupt handling capability that allow it to interface with a wide variety of peripheral devices. It also has a large library of user-written programs. The 6800D uses a single +5 V power supply and a simpler control timing signal that makes it easier to interface. The Zilog Z-80 is designed to be software-compatible with the 8080A. It has a larger instruction set and a simpler system configuration along the line of the 6800D. It uses a single +5 V power supply and a single-phase clock signal.

The microprocessors communicate with their support chips by means of communication lines called *buses*. The 8080A and 6800D use a standard bus arrangement consisting of three buses (see Fig. 1.8). The *address bus* is used to address memory and input/output devices; the *data bus* is used to transfer data in eight-bit bytes; the *control bus* is used to communicate control and status information.

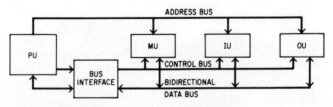

Fig. 1.8 Multiple bus architecture

The microprocessor families mentioned so far concentrate most of the computational power on single processor chips. In contrast, Fairchild's F-8 and National Semiconductor's SC/MP families distribute process and memory control operations throughout the microcomputer system. These families are designed to implement digital controllers with the fewest possible chips at the lowest cost. The member chips of these families interact so intimately that a thorough knowledge of all of them is necessary to implement a useful system.

Assessing Microprocessors

All microprocessors are described in great detail on data sheets supplied by their manufacturers. Comparison of microprocessors on the basis of this data, however, may not always lead to the best choice for an application. Although all data sheets specify a cycle time, it does not mean very much all by itself, since it is also necessary to know how much a microprocessor can accomplish in one cycle. Many processors with short cycle times end up using a good many cycles to execute quite simple instructions. The execution times of simple instructions can also be a very misleading guide since a processor executing a complex program may actually spend very little time executing simple instructions.

The number of registers in a microprocessor is not necessarily a reliable guide to its computational power. Many powerful microprocessors such as TI's 990 are deliberately designed to put all the temporary storage registers in the memory. The size of the instruction set, however, can be a useful indicator of a microprocessor's power provided the instructions are counted in a reasonable manner. Small variations of a simple instruction should not be counted as separate instructions. It is not so much the number of different instructions but the capability of these instructions that contributes to the complex data-processing capabilities of the microprocessor.

Software for Microcomputers

Collections of programs normally needed by microprocessors to carry out their tasks are commonly called *software*. Although microcomputers reduce hardware development time, they nevertheless need software to guide their operations, and the designer is still faced with the complex task of programming. Of course, the complexity of the software and the related programming effort varies from one application to the next. Simple programs for controlling traffic lights can be written and stored in approximately 8,192 (8K) words of memory (where K = 1024). However, programs for data processing for small businesses may consume all 65,536 (64K) words of memory directly addressable by commonly used microprocessors.

Most microprocessor manufacturers offer complete packages of *software development tools* such as editors, simulators, assemblers (or compilers), loaders, and debuggers. These tools, which will be discussed later, can also be obtained from independent software houses. They are available in any of the following forms: (1) built into the hardware supplied by the manufacturer, (2) stored on magnetic tape to be loaded and run on a minicomputer (*cross-computer* development systems), or (3) obtained via terminals on a time-shared computing system.

In order to be executable, instructions for a microprocessor must be written in a binary format, that is, as long strings of zeros and ones. These binary formats for instructions are called *machine languages*. Such languages are not the most suitable media for writing long error-free programs. Also, since they change from one machine to another, immense effort must be expended in the translation of programs. Hence, programs are written in languages more amenable to human comprehension and then translated into machine languages by means of some of the software development tools mentioned earlier. Descriptions of these software tools follow.

Assemblers and Compilers

Assembly languages provide designers with the opportunity to write machine language instructions in a mnemonic form that makes the instructions readily comprehensible and yet closely reflects actual machine operations. An aid called an *assembler* translates assembly-language programs into machine-language programs.

Although assembly languages are an improvement over machine languages, even they are not completely adequate for writing long, complex programs. To increase productivity and reduce program errors, programming languages closer to English—for example, FORTRAN, BASIC, and PL/1—have been designed. These are called *high-level programming languages*, and programs written in them are translated into machine languages by means of *compilers*.

Programs written in assembly languages or high-level languages are often called *source programs*, and those in machine languages are called *object programs*. Both assemblers and compilers translate source programs into object programs. Assemblers generate *program lists* that display side-by-side the source and object programs. Compilers display only the source programs because the source-program instructions do not necessarily have a one-to-one correspondence with the object-program instructions. Compilers also generate error messages and other kinds of diagnostic information for the use of the programmer.

Editors

Editors accept source programs entered through a keyboard or paper tape and transfer them to files in auxiliary memory such as magnetic tape or floppy disk. The main purpose of an editor is to help a programmer edit his source language program. Thus, on special commands from the programmer through the keyboard, an editor can add, delete, or replace portions of a source program on file.

Loaders

The operation of transferring an object program from an external storage medium, or auxiliary storage, into memory where it can be executed by a microprocessor is called *program loading*. This operation is carried out by means of a *loader*.

Debuggers

Debuggers are used to test the correct operation of object programs on microcomputers and their peripheral devices. Upon command, a debugger prints out the contents of selected locations in the memory or the processing unit. A debugger can be used to start the execution of an object program from a selected word in memory and to stop it when some predefined condition is satisfied. If the object program fails to work properly, the debugger can be used interactively to modify the object program and continue testing it.

Simulators

A *simulator* is a program that simulates the operations of a given microprocessor on a different computer. A simulator can be used to test an object program when the microprocessor hardware is unavailable. Simulators provide many of the functions provided by debuggers on real microcomputers.

Simulators allow for the manipulation and display of the contents of simulated memory units and internal registers of a microprocessor and for the set-up of break points when program execution is halted. They also collect timing information while the program is being executed.

Software Development Process

It should be clear from previous discussions that developing software for a microcomputer is as important as putting together the hardware from a kit. Normally, it is necessary to assemble the hardware only once, but new software must always be developed with every new application.

Figure 1.9 charts the software development process and shows four possible ways of developing software: (1) hand coding; (2) using a time-shared development system on a minicomputer; (3) using a dedicated cross-assembly system run on a minicomputer, and (4) using a manufacturer-supplied dedicated development system. The final testing of the object program depends on the availability of a prototype microcomputer hardware system. If one is available, the object program can be executed directly on it; otherwise, the microcomputer system must be simulated. Manufacturer-supplied development systems are usually built into hardware units; these are assembled to create a skeleton microcomputer system.

Small programs for a microcomputer can be hand-coded in machine language and stored on paper tapes. These tapes can be used to load the object program in the memory of the hardware prototype unit by means of a memory programming device (*PROM programmer*). The object program can then be tested on the hardware for possible errors. In a time-shared development system, an editor will be used to write a source program in assembly language. An assembler will then translate it into an object program. If prototype hardware is available, the object program can be tested on such hardware; otherwise, a simulator must be used to test it. In dedicated cross-computer development systems, normally running in the batch mode, the source program is punched on cards for input to the system. From that point on, the rest of the development process is similar to that of a time-shared system. Of course, if source programs are written in a high-level language, the assembler and cross-assembler must be replaced by a suitable compiler or cross-compiler.

Choice of Languages and Translators

Since the usefulness of a microcomputer system lies largely in its support software, the choice of the programming language and the language translator is critical for the designer. The basic choice lies between the use of an assembly language or a high-level language. Hand coding in a machine language is impractical for all except very small programs. The fact that an assembly language is a mnemonic form of a machine language allows the designer to take full advantage of the hardware configuration. In obtaining an assembler for assembly-language programming, the following points should be carefully considered.

The format of the assembly language supported by the assembler should be easy to use, read, and understand. The assembler should not impose stringent formatting conventions on the designer. It should allow

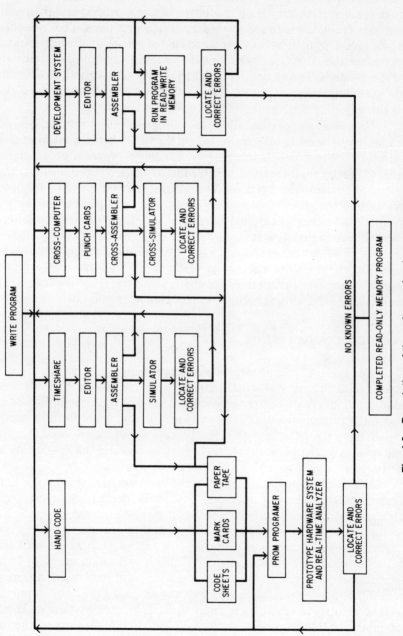

Fig. 1.9 Description of the software development process

him to use symbols for names of variables and addresses of memory words and to use arithmetic expressions for operands in a program. The latter feature frees him from the chore of evaluating every arithmetic expression in detail with assembly language instructions. The assembler should produce an alphabetically sorted list of symbols with references to the instructions that use them. This list can be a valuable debugging aid for the designer. The assembler should also flag all instructions that violate assembly language syntax and should print error messages explaining the nature of the violations.

High-level languages allow the designer many advantages not available in assembly languages, among them: (1) better control of software, (2) reduced programming cost, (3) lower program development time, (4) easier maintenance, and (5) increased portability of programs among microcomputer systems. The main disadvantage of a high-level language is that the translated object code does not always make the optimum use of microcomputer hardware, but this is not a really serious disadvantage in practice. It is one thing to improve the efficiency of short sections of object programs by assembly-language programming and quite another to write thousands of lines of error-free and efficient assembly-language instructions. In short, high-level languages are ideally suited for large programs used in complex microcomputer systems.

Microprocessor Testing

The internal complexity of a microprocessor chip makes it a difficult device to test. Nevertheless, such tests are necessary if one is to build a reliable microcomputer system. The variety of microprocessors, their unfamiliar modes of failure, and high speed of operation all directly contribute to the difficulty of the test process. Furthermore, testing at the chip level is not sufficient since there may be flaws in the fabrication of the board in which the chips are inserted.

Microprocessor testing methods can be categorized into two groups: (1) well-established test methods used with digital electronic logic circuits, and (2) test methods used with computer systems. Testing a microprocessor chip is much more complex than testing a logic circuit. First of all, the various architectures, chip layouts, pin assignments on chips, bus sizes, and so forth, make it difficult to develop standard tests. Second, the failure modes of microprocessor chips, which are different from those of logic circuits, are not well known among the users. A microprocessor chip is too complex to apply the simple stuck-at-zero/stuck-at-one model of failure used with digital logic circuits. Moreover, the information provided by microprocessor manufacturers is not detailed enough for developing such models.

Detection of microprocessor failure modes requires tests at the processor's operating speed involving a wide variety of instructions. Since access to the internal components of an LSI chip is severely restricted by pin limitations and since the microprocessor controls many of its functions internally, the tester has less control over and access to intermediate results. On the other hand, a programmable microprocessor can be thought of as a "smart" logic circuit that can aid in its own testing. Self-diagnostic programs can be used to test microprocessors without human intervention. Testing of microprocessor hardware is discussed in more detail at the end of Chap. 2.

Summary

This chapter was organized to provide an overview of the different aspects of a microcomputer system. It discusses the basic components of a digital computer along with short descriptions of several popular microcomputer families. It also describes and emphasizes the software aspects of microcomputer systems, without delving into the details but with the hope that the reader will gain some appreciation of the importance of software and software development systems. Finally, this chapter touches on microprocessor testing to alert the reader to the importance of this often ignored topic. Hardware testing will be discussed further in Chap. 2.

Chapter 2

Basic Hardware Components

Introduction

A microcomputer, like any other computer, is a *stored-program* device; it can be functionally described by the block diagram shown in Fig. 2.1. From the viewpoint of hardware, however, microcomputers are implemented entirely by means of LSI (*Large Scale Integration*) and MSI (*Medium Scale Integration*) chips, which necessitate design considerations uniquely peculiar to microcomputer architectures.

An important technical constraint on the design of the CPU (Central Processing Unit) of a microcomputer, often called a *microprocessor,* is the size of the silicon die. A microprocessor designer must develop ways to relate potential design features to their space requirements on a silicon die. The design constraints imposed by the size of the die can be circumvented by changes in the details of the manufacturing process [P-channel vs N-channel (see Appendix A)] that affect the gate density as well as the speed of operation of the circuits. For example, a Zilog Z-80 microprocessor, which uses N-channel depletion-load devices on a 185-mil-

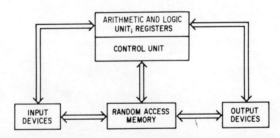

Fig. 2.1 Functional diagram of a stored-program computer

14

square die, attains three times the component density and gate speed of an Intel 4004 P-channel microprocessor on a 136-mil-square die.

Microprocessors are also required to be implemented in *dual-in-line packages* (see Appendix A) with a small number of pins. Although this requirement appears to be inconsequential, it has an enormous effect on the design of microcomputer systems. The total cost of manufacturing a large number of microprocessors is dominated by the cost of the package; hence, there is a strong incentive for using a standard package size, which, in turn, makes it difficult to design customized packages for individual microprocessors. As an example, the 18-pin package for the Intel 8008 microprocessor obliged the designers to share buses by time-multiplexing. The newer 40-pin packages allow the designer more freedom in selecting the architecture of the microprocessor.

The microprocessors implemented by MOS technology are noticeably slower than the CPU's of minicomputers. Typical instruction-execution times are of the order of 2 to 5 μs. This limitation in speed is not caused by any fundamental limitation of MOS technology but rather by the limited heat-dissipation ability of the packages. Faster microprocessors are implemented by bipolar I^{2}L technology (see Appendix A), and some of these are as powerful as a minicomputer CPU.

It should be clear from this discussion that the implementation requirements of microprocessors have important consequences for their architecture. Some general ideas about the design of a microprocessor will be discussed in the next section.

Microprocessor Architecture

A functional diagram of the basic components of a microcomputer is shown in Fig. 2.2. This is a microprogrammed microcomputer, the details of which will be discussed later. For the time being, it is sufficient to assume that the *read-only memory* (ROM) stores microinstructions

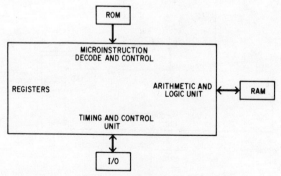

Fig. 2.2 Functional diagram of a microcomputer

used to interpret the machine language instructions stored in the *random-access memory* (RAM). In other words, the microinstruction decode and control circuitry, along with the ROM, serves the function of a hardware control unit for the system. The CPU contains *registers* for storing data and control information, an *arithmetic-logic unit* (ALU) for data processing, and necessary timing and control circuits. The CPU communicates with the ROM, RAM, and *input/output* (I/O) *devices* in order to execute programs.

Different microprocessor architectures are obtained by partitioning and distributing CPU functional units among different LSI and MSI chips. Figure 2.3 shows a single-chip microprocessor; all decoding, timing, and control circuits, the registers, the ALU, and some memory are implemented in one chip. This approach results in a relatively inflexible but inexpensive design.

Figure 2.4 shows a two-chip microprocessor. The microinstruction decode and control circuits are implemented in the ROM chip (CROM).

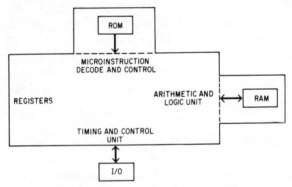

Fig. 2.3   Single-chip microprocessor

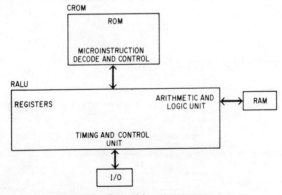

Fig. 2.4   Two-chip microprocessor

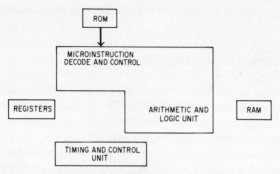

Fig. 2.5 Three-chip microprocessor

The registers and the ALU are implemented on another chip (RALU), along with the timing and control circuits. In some microprocessors, the timing and control circuits are distributed between the two chips shown in Fig. 2.4. An alternative grouping of the components can lead to a three-chip microprocessor, as shown in Fig. 2.5. By making use of more silicon area, multiple-chip designs can provide more functions; they can also reduce the need for a large number of MSI support chips for one-chip microprocessors.

The architecture of a microprocessor is a deciding factor in the selection of the bus structure of the microcomputer since the latter can seriously affect the performance of the overall system. The simplest bus structure consists of time-multiplexing a single bus for transmitting data, addresses, and control signals. A multiple-bus system uses at least one dedicated bus for data and another for addresses. Control signals may or may not use dedicated buses. In multiple-bus systems, data and addresses can be transferred simultaneously, a feature resulting in a considerable speed-up of the execution of operations. However, a multiple-bus system implies a relatively higher count of pins in the packages. Intel 8080A is an example of a multiple-bus system.

A possible microprocessor chip configuration for a multiple-bus system is shown in Fig. 2.6. The components of the microprocessor—the control unit, ALU, registers, and so forth—are built into a single CPU chip. It uses a 16-bit address bus and an 8-bit data bus to communicate

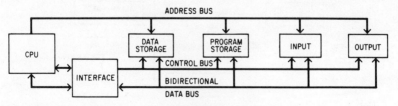

Fig. 2.6 Multiple-bus microprocessor system

with the chips storing program and data and the input/output interface chips.

Microprocessor Components

Regardless of the architecture, the processor must fetch, interpret, and execute instructions stored in the RAM and do so in a sequence specified by the program. Because of this common sequence of operations, all microprocessors contain certain common components. All microprocessors need *program counters* for storing the address of the next instruction to be fetched from the RAM; they also need *instruction registers* for storing the instruction being executed. *Accumulators* are needed for storing operands and intermediate results; various other registers may be needed for various forms of addressing schemes to be discussed later. Finally, all microprocessors must have instruction decoding logic, timing and control circuitry, an ALU and a *status or condition code register* to store various conditions resulting from the ALU operations. These basic components of a microprocessor are shown in Fig. 2.7 along with a reasonable scheme for interconnecting them.

The ALU can perform its arithmetic operations on the operands either *bit serially*—that is, one pair of bits at a time, in sequence—or *in bit parallel*—that is, all eight-bit pairs at the same time. Most ALUs of microprocessors do arithmetic operations in bit-parallel fashion. The arithmetic operations can be conducted either in the binary (using the 2's

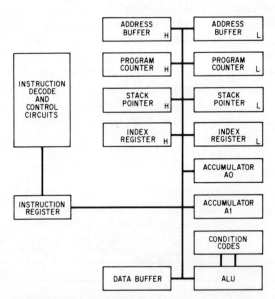

Fib. 2.7 Basic components of a microprocessor

complement system) or in the decimal number system. Some ALUs provide a choice between the two types of operations. Most microprocessor ALUs directly carry out the basic arithmetic operations of addition and subtraction. More complex operations such as multiplication and division are usually programmed into the system, either by software or by microprograms (to be discussed later). Aside from purely arithmetic operations, ALUs also provide various types of logic operations on data —for example, AND, OR, exclusive OR, bit complement, etc.—and switch operations to shift strings of bits in registers to the left or right.

A microprocessor fetches instructions and data from the random-access memory and stores results in it. To fetch or store information, a microprocessor must have registers to hold the information and other registers to hold the addresses of the words in the RAM involved in the process. Data is held in one or more accumulators, and instructions are stored one-at-a-time in an instruction register. The address of a memory word with an instruction in it is stored in a program counter. Similarly, the address of a memory word with data in it is stored in a *data counter*. Figure 2.8 shows these registers in a typical microprocessor where data and instructions are assumed to be 8 bits wide and addresses, 16 bits.

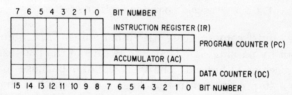

Fig. 2.8 Typical (8-bit) information storage registers and (16-bit) address storage registers in a microprocessor

There is an important difference between the operational uses of the program counter and data counter. Instructions are stored sequentially in the RAM in successive memory words. As a result, the program counter is usually incremented by a constant when it is necessary to obtain the address of the next instruction in sequence (except when the instruction being executed causes a branch in the sequence). Although the data may be stored in the RAM in a sequential manner, it is not always accessed in a sequential manner. Hence, incrementing the data counter by a suitable constant is not always very meaningful. The microprocessor logic provides the programmer with more flexibility in setting the contents of the data counter.

Microprocessor Pins and Signals

Even with the application of LSI technology, most microprocessor chips do not contain all the information they need to operate with; conse-

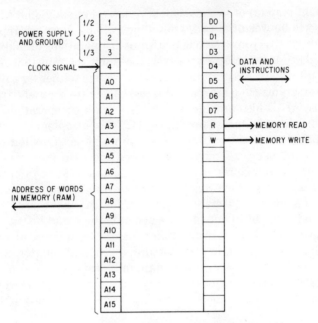

Fig. 2.9 Pins and signals on a microprocessor chip

quently, they must communicate with other chips. This communication is carried out by passing signals along the pins of the package in which the microprocessor is housed. The most popular package for a microprocessor is a 40-pin dual in-line package (DIP), which is shown in Fig. 2.9. Since the manner of use of these pins varies widely among microprocessors, only a generalized scheme will be discussed in this section.

In Fig. 2.9, the first three pins on the chip are used to provide operating power to the chip; V_1 is the current drain connection, or power input; V_2 is a current source, or ground; and V_3 is the gate voltage (not required in some chips). Figure 2.10(A) shows a commonly used arrangement for the power supply to a chip; two power supplies of $+5$ V and $+12$ V and a single ground connection are needed. Figure 2.10(B) shows an alternative arrangement that uses a single power source of $+5$ V. The fourth pin in Fig. 2.10 is used to introduce the external master clock signal needed by the internal timing circuitry of the microprocessor.

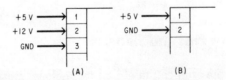

Fig. 2.10 (a) Two-power sources, and (b) single-power source

A microprocessor transmits the addresses of memory words to the RAM chip to obtain instructions and data. The number of bits needed to specify an address depends on the total number of words directly addressable by the microprocessor. If this number is assumed to be 65,536 (64K), then 16 bits are needed to specify an address. In Fig. 2.9, the 16 pins marked A0, A1, . . ., A15 are used for addressing memory. Inside a microprocessor, data and instructions are stored in various registers; some pins on the microprocessor chip are dedicated to transmitting data and instructions in and out of the microprocessor. Commonly, data and instructions are coded in 8-bit bytes. The pins marked D0, . . ., D7 in Fig. 2.9 are used for transmitting data and instructions.

A microprocessor can either fetch instructions and data from the RAM or store data in the RAM. The process of obtaining information from the RAM is called a *memory-read operation;* the process of storing information in the RAM is called a *memory-write operation.* The microprocessor provides the RAM with a read or write signal, along with the address of a memory word, to indicate the direction of flow of information; the pins marked R and W in Fig. 2.9 are used for this purpose.

Clearly, the signals that have been described and the pins that are allocated to these signals are absolutely necessary for a microprocessor's operation. The pins that are yet to be assigned transmit other signals; these will be discussed in later sections.

ROM and RAM Memory Chips

Except for single-chip microcomputers, instructions and data used by a microprocessor are stored in LSI memory chips external to the microprocessor. Even single-chip microcomputers may need to expand their memory capacity by incorporating external memory chips. Logically, a memory chip can be thought of as a linearly ordered arrangement of words, as shown in Fig. 2.11, where each word can store a string of binary digits or bits. Each word has a unique address to identify it whenever strings of bits are read from or written into that word. All memory chips normally used with microprocessors are of the random-access variety— that is, the time required to access any arbitrary word in the memory is independent of the address of the word.

A read-only memory (ROM) chip has the property that every bit string is written into the corresponding word during the process of manufacture. These bit strings are permanent and cannot be altered in any way by a microprocessor using the ROM. An *EPROM* is an electrically programmable read-only memory whose contents can be erased by prolonged exposure to ultra-violet light and new bit strings stored by special programming devices. The contents cannot be changed, however, by a microprocessor under normal operating conditions.

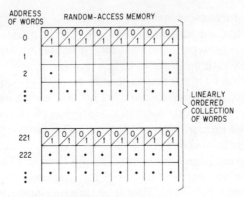

ADDRESS
OF WORDS   RANDOM-ACCESS MEMORY

LINEARLY
ORDERED
COLLECTION
OF WORDS

Fig. 2.11 Functional description of a random-access memory showing words, addresses, and bit strings

Usually, the number of words stored in a ROM chip is much less than the number of words addressable by a microprocessor. For example, microprocessors normally use 16-bit addresses that allow them to address 65,536 (64K) words directly, whereas ROM chips contain 4,096 (4K), 1,024 (1K), or fewer words. Consequently, several ROM chips are used concurrently to provide as much ROM address space as a microprocessor may use. The higher order address bits (six) are used to select one among the many available ROM chips, and the lower order bits (ten) are used to address specific words in the selected ROM chip. Figure 2.12 shows such an arrangement of two ROM chips, each containing 1K words of eight bits each. Select bits 000000 select ROM #0, and select bits 000001 select ROM #1. Upon receiving a READ signal from the microprocessor, only the selected ROM chip outputs the bit string contained in the addressed word onto the data lines. The time spent by the microprocessor in reading the contents of a word in a random-access memory is called a *read cycle*. The timing of signals during a typical read cycle is shown in Fig. 2.13.

This timing diagram shows the sequence of events—that is, the changes of signal levels—that occur during a read cycle. The arrows are used to establish a cause-and-effect relationship among these events; the tails start at the causes and the heads end at the effects. In order to read the contents of a memory word, the microprocessor transmits the address of the word on address lines A0, . . . , A15. After a suitable time interval, t_1, the microprocessor lowers the READ signal to command the selected memory chip to start the memory read operation. The time interval t_1 is used to propagate the address down the address lines to all the memory chips, to latch the address bits onto the internal address registers of all memory chips, and to select a particular chip from the rest. During time interval t_2, a memory read operation is carried out by the selected memory chip. Prior to the end of t_2, the data on data lines D0, . . . , D7 is

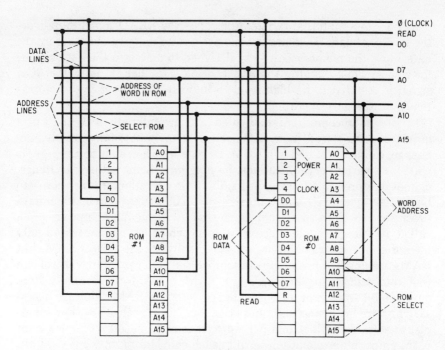

Fig. 2.12 Connection of two ROM chips

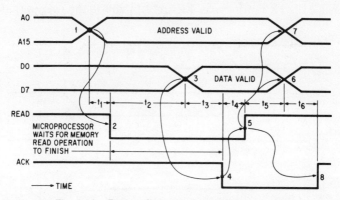

Fig. 2.13 Timing diagram of a typical read cycle

indeterminate. After the end of t_3, data bits coming from the memory chip onto the data lines are stable. At that instant, the acknowledgement line ACK is lowered by the memory chip to inform the microprocessor that data has been fetched and is stable on the data lines. Until it receives the ACK signal, the microprocessor normally waits for the completion of the memory read operation. The memory chip must maintain the signals on the data lines until the microprocessor reacts to its ACK signal. During time period t_4, the microprocessor transfers the data from the data lines to an internal register and raises the READ signal to indicate the receipt of data. To guard against premature removal of data from the data lines, the memory chips are designed to maintain the data signals for a short while (t_5) after the READ signal goes high. Finally, the ACK signal is restored to its high level to indicate that the memory chip is ready for the next operation.

If a microcomputer is dedicated to a particular application, its program may be stored in a ROM. Even then, input data, which may change, cannot be stored in a ROM. In general, when a microcomputer is used for a variety of applications, its programs, being subject to change, cannot be stored in a ROM. For flexibility in operation, it is necessary to have memory chips in which bit strings can be written into by the microprocessor as well as read from. Such *read/write* memory chips are often called RAMs (Random Access Memory chips). Note that read-only memories are also random-access—that is, ROMs are always RAMs but RAMs are not ROMs since a microprocessor under program control can write bit strings into the words of a RAM. A RAM can normally store only one bit in each of its words; hence, multiple RAM chips are necessary to store bit strings with more than one bit in each string. For example, to store eight data bits per word, it may be necessary to use eight RAM chips in parallel, each word in each chip storing only one data bit.

The time spent by a microprocessor to write a bit string into a word of RAM is called a *write cycle*. Figure 2.14 shows the events that occur

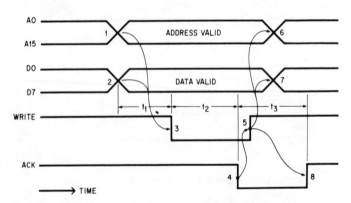

Fig. 2.14   Timing diagram of a typical write cycle

during a typical write cycle. To start a memory write operation, a microprocessor outputs the address of the RAM word and the data on the address lines (A0, . . . , A15) and the data lines (D0, . . . , D15), respectively. After a time period, t_1, while the signal values settle down, the microprocessor lowers the WRITE signal, thus indicating the start of a memory write operation. The time period t_2 is used by the RAM chips to write the data into the addressed word. The completion of the memory write operation is signaled by the lowering of the ACK signal. After receiving the ACK signal, the microprocessor raises the WRITE signal and floats the address and data lines. The raising of the WRITE signal is followed by the raising of the ACK signal, indicating that the RAM chip is ready for the next memory operation (read or write).

Instruction Execution

The control unit of a microprocessor fetches machine-language instructions, or *macroinstructions,* from the random-access memory and decodes and executes them. The operations carried out by a control unit in order to fetch and execute a macroinstruction are called *micro-operations.* The sequencing of these micro-operations are controlled primarily by a crystal clock with a period that may vary from a hundred nanoseconds (10^{-9} s) to a microsecond (10^{-6} s). Periodic clock signals are usually denoted by ϕ; one such signal is shown in Fig. 2.15(A).

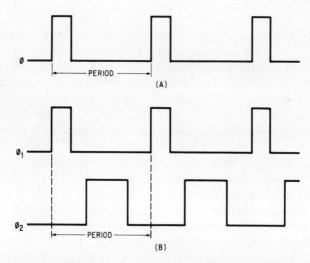

Fig. 2.15 (a) Clock signal ϕ, and (b) two-phase clock signal (ϕ_1, ϕ_2)

The crystal oscillator is external to the microprocessor, but the circuits that generate the clock signal may or may not be on the same chip as the microprocessor. Some microprocessors use a more complex two-phase (ϕ_1, ϕ_2) clock signal, shown in Fig. 2.15(B). The simple clock signal provides two edges and two states per period, whereas the two-phase clock signal has four edges and three states (see Fig. 2.16).

The time taken by a control unit to fetch and execute a macroinstruction is called an *instruction cycle.* Every instruction cycle is

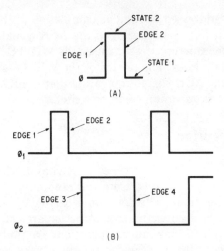

Fig. 2.16 (a) Edge 1: leading or positive edge; Edge 2: trailing or negative edge, and (b) State 1: $\phi_1 = 0$, ϕ_2; State 2: $\phi_1 = 0$, $\phi_2 = 1$; State 3: $\phi_1 = 1$, $\phi_2 = 0$

divided into at least two parts: the *fetch phase* and the *execute phase.* During the fetch phase, a macroinstruction is fetched from the RAM or ROM, deposited in the instruction register (IR) in the control unit, and decoded for execution. The address of the macroinstruction in the memory to be fetched is provided by the contents of the program counter (PC). During the execute phase of the instruction cycle, the macroinstruction stored in the IR is executed by means of a sequence of micro-operations. These micro-operations are elementary operations that are carried out directly by the control unit by means of electrical signals. A typical sequence of micro-operations carried out to complement the contents of the accumulator would be as follows:

1. Transfer the contents of the AC to the internal data bus
2. Transfer the contents of the internal data bus to the ALU
3. Activate complementing logic in the ALU
4. Transfer the output of the ALU to the internal data bus
5. Transfer the contents of the internal data bus to the AC

The timing diagram of an instruction fetch of a typical microprocessor using a clock signal ϕ is shown in Fig. 2.17. During clock period T_0, the leading edge of ϕ transfers the contents of PC onto the address lines A0, . . ., A15. It may also set an output signal IFTCH high to indicate an instruction fetch phase. The trailing edge of ϕ in T_0 sets the output signal READ high to request a memory read operation.

During T_1, the microprocessor waits for the instruction bits to be fetched and put on data lines D0, . . ., D7. The leading edge of ϕ in T_2

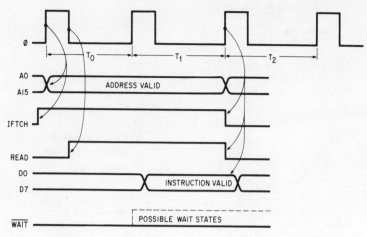

Fig. 2.17 Timing diagram of an instruction fetch operation

transfers the instruction bits from the data bus into the microprocessor. It also resets the IFTCH and the READ output signals.

In some systems, the memory may need more time to output an instruction on the data bus than that allowed during T_1. In such cases, the microprocessor enters a *wait state* after T_1, and the $\overline{\text{WAIT}}$ signal input from the timing circuit is lowered. Upon receiving an acknowledgement of the completion of a memory read (the ACK signal in Fig. 2.13), the timing circuit restores the $\overline{\text{WAIT}}$ signal. The microprocessor samples the $\overline{\text{WAIT}}$ signal during every T_1 period while it is in the wait state. When the $\overline{\text{WAIT}}$ signal is restored, the microprocessor uses the leading edge of ϕ during the next T_2 period to transfer the instruction on the data bus into the instruction register. An updated version of the microprocessor chip shown in Fig. 2.9 is given in Fig. 2.18 with additional pin assignments included.

During T_0, T_1, and T_2, an instruction is fetched from memory and deposited in the IR. The instruction is now decoded by the decoding circuits internal to a microprocessor. Then, during T_3, the program counter is incremented, marking the end of an instruction fetch phase.

Parallel Input/Output Ports

A microprocessor can transfer eight bits of data simultaneously over eight data lines to all input/output devices. Some peripheral devices, however, can receive or transmit only one bit at a time. Such devices, called *serial devices,* will be discussed in the next section. Since parallel devices, on the other hand, can transfer eight bits of data, they are easier to interface with a microprocessor. Peripheral devices are not

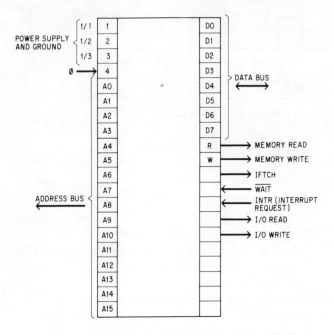

Fig. 2.18 Additional signals and pin assignments on a microprocessor chip

directly connected to the data and control buses of a microcomputer system but rather to input/output *ports* that provide for data buffering and the transfer of control signals.

A *parallel input/output port* can be functionally described as in Fig. 2.19. Each port in the figure consists of a *control register, a data buffer register,* and control circuits. The microprocessor uses the data bus to store commands for the device controllers in the control registers. These commands control the mode of operation of the ports while they are active in transferring data. The data bus is thus shared by the control commands and the data.

In order to transfer data, a microprocessor must identify the port

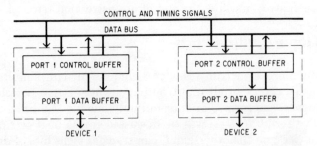

Fig. 2.19 Parallel input/output ports

to be used for the transfer. For this purpose, each port must have a unique *identification number.* The identification number can be transmitted over the address bus and decoded by each port; only the port selected by the number needs to acknowledge and respond. If the registers in a port can be directly addressed, they can be considered as an extension of the random-access memory rather than as arbitrary identification numbers. Such an approach, called *memory mapped I/O,* simplifies the job of writing input/output routines using regular memory transfer instructions and also eliminates the need for specialized input/output instructions.

The speed of operation of a microprocessor and of the peripheral devices differs by several orders of magnitude. To make the best use of their capabilities, each of these devices and the microprocessor operate at their own speeds and in an asynchronous manner. Thus, synchronization signals between a device and a microprocessor must precede any data transfer operation to insure that data is not lost in the process of transfer. A synchronization scheme commonly used in microcomputer systems, called *handshaking,* is shown in the timing diagrams of Fig. 2.20.

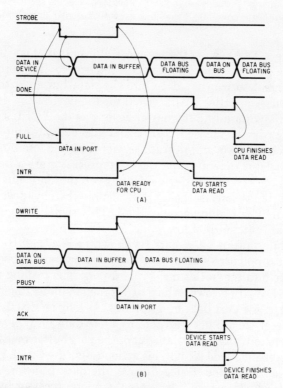

Fig. 2.20 Timing diagram (a) for data input via a port, and (b) for data output via a port

When a port involved in a data transfer is ready, it signals the microprocessor by means of an *interrupt signal* (INTR). Subsequently, at a suitable point in time, the microprocessor acknowledges the interrupt request. Upon acknowledging an interrupt request, the microprocessor suspends execution of the current program, stores contents of all registers in memory, and starts execution of a program to service the interrupt request. When the service program terminates, the microprocessor restores the contents of all registers and continues with the execution of the interrupted program. This sequence of events is shown in Fig. 2.21.

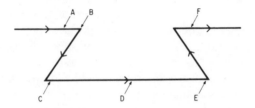

Fig. 2.21   An interrupt processing sequence (A: interrupt occurs; B: interrupt acknowledged; C: save register contents; D: execute service routing; E: restore register contents; F: continue execution of interrupted program)

Figure 2.20(A) shows the sequence of events that occurs during input of data via a port. The device attached to the port lowers the STROBE signal to transfer data into the data buffer of the port. The STROBE raises a buffer FULL signal for the device; the device should not transfer any data into the buffer as long as the FULL signal is high. The trailing edge of the STROBE signal also activates interrupt signal INTR, which requests an interrupt service from the microprocessor. After acknowledging the interrupt, the microprocessor executes an instruction that transfers the buffer contents over the data bus. When this transfer starts, it lowers the DONE signal, thereby deactivating the INTR signal. The trailing edge of the DONE signal restores the buffer FULL signal to its normal low value.

For data output via a port, as shown in Fig. 2.20(B), the bus interface logic, upon a request from the microprocessor, strobes data from the data bus into the buffer register of a port. The trailing edge of data write signal DWRITE lowers the PBUSY signal, indicating to the microprocessor that the port data buffer is full. As long as PBUSY is low, the microprocessor should not transfer any more data into that port. As the devices starts to transfer the data out of the port buffer register, it lowers acknowledgement signal ACK. This action resets the PBUSY signal to its normal value. After the device finishes the data transfer, it raises the ACK signal, which in turn interrupts the microprocessor by raising the

INTR signal. The microprocessor, in response to the interrupt from the port, can take whatever actions are necessary.

Serial Input/Output Ports

In a microcomputer system, a *serial input/output port* is used to interface with those peripheral devices (magnetic cassettes, teletypes, etc.) that can transfer data only in a serial fashion, that is, one bit at a time. Data transfers over the data bus are always in a parallel format, that is, several bits at a time. Serial input/output ports are used to convert data formats from parallel to serial and from serial to parallel, respectively. A functional diagram of such a port is shown in Fig. 2.22. The data-in and data-out paths shown here are double-buffered. Serial data is accepted, and shifted in one bit at a time, into input buffer I1 and assembled into a multibit data format. When I1 is full, its contents are transferred, all bits in parallel, into the I2 buffer. While the next multibit

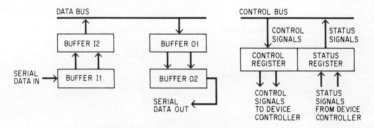

Fig. 2.22   Serial input/output port

data is being assembled in I1, the microprocessor must transfer the contents of I2 out of I2; otherwise, they will be lost when the next data byte is transferred in from I1. This sequence of transfers is shown in Fig. 2.23 (A). Multibit parallel data from the data bus is transferred into the O1 buffer by the microprocessor. The contents of O1 are transferred, all bits in parallel, into O2 when it is ready to be transmitted. The contents of O2 are shifted out, one bit at a time, in a serial manner to the peripheral device. The sequence of events in data output is shown in Fig. 2.23(B).

In serial transmission of data, all bits are transmitted in a sequence over the same line. The signal at the receiver may appear as shown in Fig. 2.24(A). In order to identify the bit pattern transmitted, the receiver must know where one bit ends and the next begins, that is, the bit boundaries (see Fig. 2.24 B). To identify the bit boundaries, the receiver must know the rate, in bits per second (BPS), at which the bits are being transmitted and also some starting point along the time-axis. Once the transmission rate is known, the receiver uses a clock that is faster than the

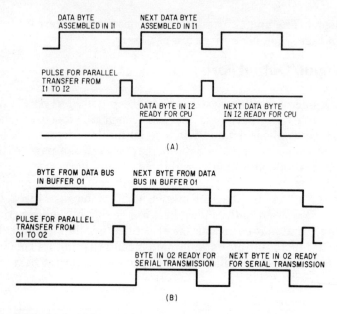

Fig. 2.23 (a) Serial input of data into microprocessor, and (b) serial output of data from microprocessor

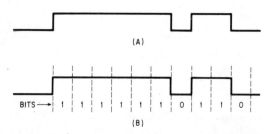

Fig. 2.24 (a) Input signal at the receiver, and (b) example of a bit pattern in an input signal

transmitter and subdivides the basic bit-period into a number of subintervals (see Fig. 2.25). The incoming bits are then shifted into the receiver's buffer register at approximately the middle of a bit period. This approach avoids the problems that would otherwise arise because of the finite settling time of the incoming bits. If the period of the receiver's clock is much shorter then the bit period, then it is not necessary to synchronize the clock accurately with respect to the transmitter. It is not necessary to know the exact midpoint of the bit period; a good approximation is sufficient for the receiver.

Serial data transmitters operate either in the *asynchronous mode* or in the *synchronous mode.* In the asynchronous mode, data is trans-

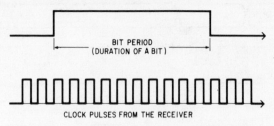

Fig. 2.25 Dividing a bit-period into subintervals

mitted only when it is available and ready for transmission. When no data bits are being transmitted, the transmitter holds the data line at a constant high value. When transmission starts, the transmitter lowers the data line, and this high-to-low transition signals the receiver of the start of the transmission. This signal is often called *marking the start of a data byte.* In the asynchronous mode, as shown in Fig. 2.26, the transmitter starts the transmission with a start bit and ends the transmission of every data byte with a parity-check bit for error detection and one or two stop bits. Thus, every data byte transmitted in an asynchronous mode is framed within certain start and stop bits.

Fig. 2.26 Asynchronous serial transmission (M: mark; S: start bit; P: parity bit; T0, T1: stop bits)

In the synchronous mode, the transmitter continuously transmits; in the absence of data bits, it transmits some preassigned synchronization character. Start of a data byte transmission is denoted by two such synchronization characters followed by some mark such as a high-to-low transition. Normally, the receiver enters a hunting mode, in which it searches for two synchronization characters followed by a mark in the input stream. When it detects the start of a data-byte transmission in this manner, it shifts the data bits into its buffer register and assembles the data byte for transfer to the data bus.

Figure 2.27 shows the timing diagram of data output through a serial port. After data byte is valid on data bus, INO1 is used to transfer data into the O1 buffer. The same pulse is used to lower O1EMPTY to indicate that O1 contains a data byte. A new data byte transferred into O1 when O1EMPTY is low will destroy existing data. When previous serial transmission out of O2 is complete, O2EMPTY is raised, indicating that buffer O2 is empty. The contents of O1 are then transferred into O2 by the INO2 pulse. INO2 also lowers O2EMPTY and raises O1EMPTY,

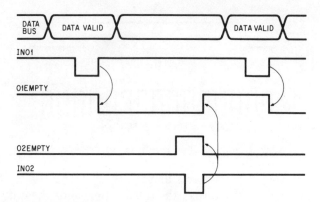

Fig. 2.27 Timing diagram of serial data output

indicating that buffer O1 is empty. INO1 is now used once again to transfer the next byte from the data bus into O1.

Priority Arbitration

As explained earlier, the synchronization of operations among the microprocessor and the peripheral devices is carried out by means of interrupt signals. When more than one peripheral device is in operation, it is possible for multiple interrupt signals to arrive at the microprocessor at the same time. Since the microprocessor can service only one interrupt at a time, it is necessary to assign *priorities of service* to the different interrupt requests. The simplest approach is to assign a fixed priority of service to each interrupt signal. A priority interrupt control chip, using this principle, is shown in Fig. 2.28. The incoming interrupt signals are denoted by I0, I1, . . . , I7; the outgoing interrupt signal to the microprocessor chip is INT. The signals A0, A1, and A2 output the identification number (in binary) of the pending highest priority interrupt among I0, . . . I7. The microprocessor can *disable* the whole interrupt

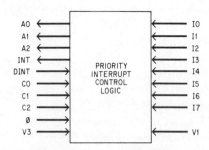

Fig. 2.28 Priority interrupt control chip

system by means of DINT. Such interrupt control chips normally contain an internal control register. By storing suitable control words in this register, groups of interrupts can be selectively disabled. Input lines C0, ..., C2 are used to transfer control words into this register.

Programmable Counter/Timer

In microcomputer applications, where it is often necessary to monitor external events in real time, a programmable counter/timer is a very useful device. A functional description of such a counter/timer is shown in Fig. 2.29. The counter/timer can be addressed and accessed either as a memory location or an input/output port. The initial value of the 16-bit binary counter can be set under program control. With every clock pulse, the contents of the counter is decremented by one. If the clock pulse is derived from a periodic clock, the result is a *programmable timer*. On the other hand, if it is derived from some aperiodic external signal, the device becomes an *external-event counter*. The start signal to initiate the timer/counter can be generated either by hardware or software. Whenever the count reaches zero, the device transmits an output signal to indicate an end of count.

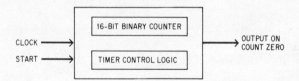

Fig. 2.29   Programmable counter/timer

Microprogrammed Microprocessors

The micro-operations within the control unit can be carried out in two different manners. They can either be executed by combinational and/or sequential logic circuits that are activated by the decoded contents of the IR and sequenced by the clock signal, or they can be carried out by means of microprograms. The first approach results in a relatively inflexible hardware control unit.

As an example of the hardware approach, consider the execution of three branch macroinstructions: JMP (unconditional jump), JAZ (conditional jump when the contents of AC equal zero), and JAM (conditional jump when the contents of AC are negative). The addresses in the RAM for the jumps are provided as part of the instructions and can be obtained from the IR. The jumps can be executed by the following micro-operations:

1. Transferring the address from the IR to the internal data bus
2. Transferring the address from the internal data bus to the PC

For JAZ and JAM, the second micro-operation is executed only when the specified conditions are satisfied.

A hardware logic circuit for the execution of the second micro-operation is shown in Fig. 2.30. In this figure, AZ = 1 only if the contents of AC = 0. Similarly AM = 1 only if the contents of AC are negative. The output of the circuit provides the load signal that transfers the address from the internal data bus to the PC. If the output of the instruction decoder JMP = 1, then when the timing signal arrives, a load signal will be generated for the PC. On the other hand, if JAZ = 1 (JAM = 1) and AZ = 1 (AM = 1), only then will a load signal for PC be generated by the arrival of the timing signal. However, if AZ = 0 (AM = 0), no such load signal will be sent to the PC during the execution of JAZ (JAM).

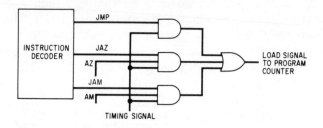

Fig. 2.30 Hardware for executing a microinstruction

In a hardware control unit, every micro-operation is carried out by means of hardware circuits similar to the one shown in Fig. 2.30. The *macroinstructions* or *machine language instructions* are decoded to select and activate the appropriate hardware circuits in the control unit. Just as macroinstructions are coded and stored in the RAM as binary strings, micro-operations can also be coded and stored in memory. A sequence of such micro-operations is called a *microinstruction;* every macro-instruction can be represented by a *microprogram* which consists of a sequence of microinstructions needed to execute that macroinstruction. The binary operation code (*opcode*) of a macroinstruction can be de-coded to find the address of the first microinstruction in the micro-program representing that macroinstruction. The control unit then fetches and executes the microinstructions from the microprogram stored in a memory. With the completion of the execution of the micro-program, the overall effect appears to be that of the execution of the macroinstruction represented by that microprogram. Since some of the bits representing a micro-operation in a microinstruction can be used directly (or with very little coding) to provide the necessary control sig-

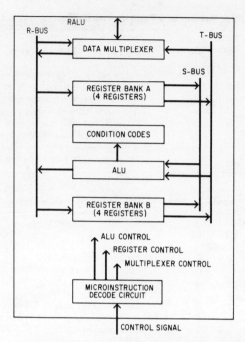

Fig. 2.31 A hypothetical RALU chip

nals, the complexity of the hardware circuits needed for that purpose are very much reduced.

As an example of a microprogrammed microprocessor, consider a hypothetical arrangement of registers and ALU on a chip called RALU, as shown in Fig. 2.31. It has eight identical registers, divided into two groups of four registers each. Contents of the R-Bus can be stored in any register, and register contents can be loaded either on the S-Bus or T-Bus. The data multiplexer can input data from outside the chip onto the R-Bus or output data either from the T-Bus or R-Bus. The ALU can carry out add, subtract, shift-left, shift-right, complement, AND, OR, and exclusive-OR operations. The microinstruction decode circuit on the RALU chip reduces the number of pins used by the control signals.

A register in each register bank is identified by a number from 0 to 3 that requires two binary digits. The store and load operations of a register are specified by two more binary digits. Table 2.1 shows the codes for the specification of a register in bank A and its control signals. In this table, bits B0 and B1 are obviously used to identify a register and B2 and B3 are used to specify its control signal (load or store). Since there are two groups of registers, eight bits will be needed to specify all the registers involved in a micro-operation. As shown in Table 2.2, four bits are needed to specify all the operations of the ALU.

Table 2.1 Specification of a Register and Its Control Signals in Bank A

B3	B2	B1	B0	Specifications
		Code		
0	0	0	0	Store contents of R-Bus in register 0
0	1	0	0	Load S-Bus with contents of register 0
1	0	0	0	Load T-Bus with contents of register 0
0	0	0	1	Store contents of R-Bus in register 1
0	1	0	1	Load S-Bus with contents of register 1
1	0	0	0	Load T-Bus with cotents of register 1
—	—	—	—	
1	1	1	1	No operations with registers in bank A

Table 2.2 Specification of the ALU Operations

B11	B10	B9	B8	Specifications
	Code			
0	0	0	0	Disable ALU output
1	0	1	0	Load ALU output on R-Bus
1	1	0	0	Add
1	1	0	1	Subtract
1	1	1	0	Left-shift contents of T-Bus by one bit
1	1	1	1	Right-shift contents of T-Bus by one bit
1	0	1	1	Complement contents of T-Bus
1	0	1	0	AND
1	0	0	1	OR
1	1	0	1	Exlusive-OR

Table 2.3 Specification of Data Multiplexer Operations

B14	B13	B12	Specifications
	Code		
0	0	0	No operation
0	0	1	Transfer data from T-Bus to external bus
0	1	0	Transfer data from R-Bus to external bus
1	0	0	Transfer data from external bus to R-Bus

Table 2.4 Sample Microinstructions

Micro-instructions	Bit numbers														
	14	13	12	11	10	9	8	7	6	5	4	3	2	1	0
1	0	0	0	1	1	0	0	1	0	1	1	0	1	0	1
2	0	0	0	1	0	1	0	1	1	1	1	0	0	0	1
3	1	0	0	0	0	0	0	0	0	0	1	0	0	1	0
4	0	1	0	1	0	1	0	1	1	1	1	1	1	1	1

The five possible operations of the data multiplexer are specified by bits B12, B13, and B14, as shown in Table 2.3. Some typical microinstructions, built out of the coded micro-operations shown in Tables 2.1 through 2.3, are given in Table 2.4.

Microinstruction 1 adds the contents of register 1 in bank A and register 3 in bank B; microinstruction 2 stores the ALU output in register 1 in bank A via the R-Bus. Together, these two microinstructions can define an ADD macroinstruction. Microinstruction 3 loads register 2 in bank A with data from outside via the R-Bus. Microinstruction 4 transfers the output of the ALU to the external bus via the R-Bus.

Microprograms are stored in a separate read-only memory (ROM), which may or may not be part of the control unit. A microprogram in a ROM is permanent and cannot be altered by writing new information in it. In some microprocessors, the microinstruction decode and control circuits are built into the ROM chip, which is then called a *control ROM*, or *CROM*.

Macroinstructions are coded to provide the addresses of the first instruction of the microprograms in the ROM representing the corresponding macroinstructions (see Fig. 2.32). This approach requires that arbitrary operation codes of macroinstructions be transformed into convenient control store addresses. This transformation can be per-

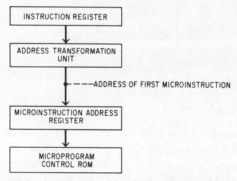

Fig. 2.32 Addressing of the first microinstruction in a microprogram

formed by means of logic gates and multiplexers, but the choice of operation codes and starting addresses in ROM are somewhat limited by the need to minimize logical complexity. Alternative methods of transformations are based on the use of programmable logic arrays (PLAs); one such scheme is shown in Fig. 2.33.

All microprogrammed microprocessors also incorporate a microprogram sequencer shown in Fig. 2.34. The purpose of the sequencer is to sequence the microinstructions in the ROM that form microprograms,

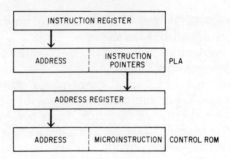

Fig. 2.33　Use of PLAs for address transformation

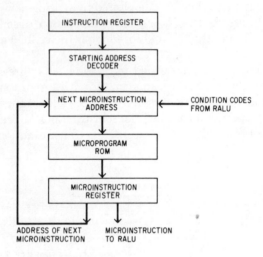

Fig. 2.34　A microprogram sequencer

representing macroinstructions. The sequencer receives the starting address of a microinstruction by decoding the operation code of the macroinstruction in the IR. Subsequent microinstruction addresses are usually provided by the microinstructions being executed. The condition codes from the RALU are also used in the selection of the next microinstruction to be executed.

Chip-Slice Architectures

A *chip-slice,* itself a simple RALU, is best considered as a building block of arbitrary microprocessors (that is, CPUs). The basic idea is to design a simple RALU chip, such that several such RALU chips can be put together to form a complex RALU. The set of simple RALU chips are

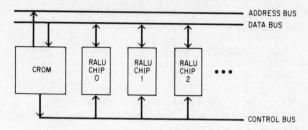

Fig. 2.35 Chip-sliced microprocessor

controlled by a microprogrammed CROM as shown in Fig. 2.35, resulting in a more complex microprocessor. Since arbitrary macroinstruction sets can be implemented by microprogramming, any arbitrary microprocessor can be built, in principle at least, by the chip-slice approach. This section will be concerned with the design principles of a chip-slice.

A basic chip-slice is designed so that it can operate in parallel with other similar chip-slices to create a complex system. If the architecture of chip-slices is chosen to reflect the architecture of a conventional microprocessor, such as that shown in Fig. 2.8, it will be very difficult to operate them in parallel. To design a chip-slice, those components of a microprocessor that have a certain uniformity about them must be separated from the other components that are highly specialized. The control unit of a microprocessor, shown in Fig. 2.36, is one of the most specialized units in the system. Since the logical complexity of combining and operating such control units in parallel is enormous, a common sense solution to the problem is to leave the control unit out of a basic chip-slice design. This approach, of course, leaves the registers and the ALU portion of the CPU, which can be organized in a standard arrangement such as that shown in Fig. 2.31 to form a chip-slice RALU.

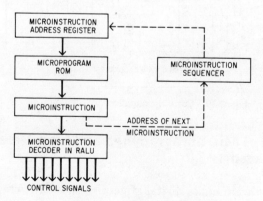

Fig. 2.36 Control unit of a microprogrammed microprocessor

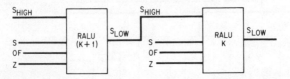

Fig. 2.37 Signals that must be shared by chip-slices [S_{LOW}, S_{HIGH}: low- [and high-order bits of the shifter; S: signbit; OF: overflow indicator; Z: zero indicator (for the accumulator)]

In order to operate in parallel, each chip-slice must output certain signals (see Fig. 2.37) for external use by the control unit and for transmission from one chip-slice to the next. The least and most significant bits of the shifter must be available externally so that they can be transmitted from one chip-slice to the next to form a long shifter. The sign bit and the overflow indicator bit of the accumulator must also be available; these bits, transferred out of the chip-slice handling the most significant digits of the microprocessor data, can then be used to indicate the status of arithmetic operations. The signal indicating the accumulator contents to be zero for each chip-slice must be ORed externally to create an overall zero status indicator for the microprocessor. Finally, the carry bit generated by each chip-slice as a result of addition must be propagated to the next higher order chip-slice. The carry bit cannot be propagated sequentially since the chip-slices must operate in parallel. Hence, external carry look-ahead logic, as shown in Fig. 2.38, must be used to provide the carry inputs for the chip-slices.

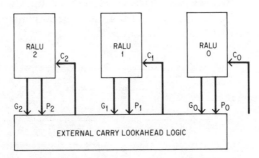

Fig. 2.38 Carry propagation between chip slices

Discussion of Microprogrammed and Chip-Slice Microprocessors

Any programmable digital system, such as a microprocessor, has many advantages over hard-wired logic. By a simple change of programs stored in a RAM, the same processor can be used for different applications. Microprogramming enhances this inherent advantage by allowing designers to tailor or optimize the same hardware for different applications. Increased execution speed compared to that of conventional machine language programs is one of the major benefits of microprograms. Other benefits are proprietary designs that are hard to copy, macroinstruction sets tailored to reduce memory requirements, emulation of existing systems, and so on.

Basic features of the system architecture such as data length, register allocation, and interrupt structure can be changed by microprogramming. Microprogramming of application programs can eliminate the memory required to store macroinstructions, the time needed to fetch and decode them, and the registers required to store and address them.

Increase in speed of execution contributes directly to the reduction of system response time. In the case of interrupt handling, the total time required to detect an interrupt, to identify the interrupting device, and to branch to the appropriate service routine can sometimes be reduced by as much as three-fourths by replacing conventional machine language programs by microprograms. Other complex operations such as multiplication, division, and subroutine calls can be accomplished faster by using microprograms.

An important application of microprogramming involves the design of the control units for chip-slice microprocessors. Microprogrammed chip-slice architecture provides the user with the benefits of a custom-designed microprocessor at a fraction of its cost and development time and with a higher probability of meeting design specifications. The user can freely choose the data length, register allocation, instruction set, and input/output interfaces. The possibility of using a standard set of chip-slices for the design of different microprocessors is a boon to both the users and the chip manufacturers. Many users have a need of several different classes of microprocessors across their product lines. This may call for 4-bit processors with BCD arithmetic operations, 8-bit processors for handling ASCII characters, and more complex 16- or 24-bit processors for advanced data handling capabilities. All these processors can be built out of 4-bit RALU chips with specialized CROMs.

The simplest approach to the utilization of chip-slice architecture consists of incorporating some user-designed instructions in additional CROMs into a standard chip-slice design. This approach allows the user to customize a microprocessor design while retaining the use of the standard assembler, loader, editor, debugger, and the like, that were developed for the standard design. Use of a standard product also allows concurrent development of the hardware input/output interfaces, software, and additional CROMs. A less expensive approach in terms of development effort is to emulate an existing system. A more expensive approach is for the user to develop a specialized chip-level design. The user has complete freedom in structuring the system but must also define an instruction set, develop all microprograms, build and debug hardware, generate tests for the customized CROMs, and finally develop all support software.

Single-Chip Microcomputer

A microprocessor by itself cannot form a microcomputer; it acts only as a CPU and needs other support chips to store programs and data, provide interfaces with input/output devices, and the like. The difficulty of interconnecting all these chips are eliminated and the application of microcomputers is simplified if all the functions of the support chips are built into the microprocessor chip itself. Such a chip is more than a microprocessor; it is a microcomputer, being directly attached to the device controllers of the input/output devices to form a complete microcomputer system.

A major objective in the design of a single-chip microcomputer is to access a RAM within a fraction of an instruction cycle so that instructions requiring multiple RAM access are executed in one instruction cycle. When such a single-chip microcomputer is used as controller, it interfaces directly with input/output devices. In this case, the speed of execution is limited only by the speed of the chip, since operations such as fetching of instructions from an external RAM through a shared bus (see Fig. 2.6) are eliminated. Technological advances in the construction of the microcomputer chip are easily transferred to a microcomputer system that uses a single chip for implementation.

The block diagram of a typical single-chip microcomputer is shown in Fig. 2.39. The microprocessor in the chip operates either in eight-bit or in four-bit mode and computes either in the pure binary number system or in the decimal system, using BCD representations. The registers used by the ALU and the memory for storage of data are integrated into a single RAM section, as shown in Fig. 2.40, to provide the programmer with maximum flexibility. The chip also incorporates a ROM and an electrically programmable ROM (EPROM) for storing programs. The

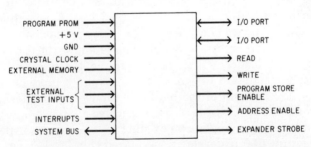

Fig. 2.39 A typical single-chip microcomputer

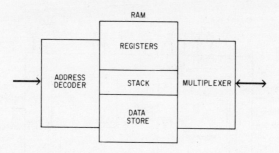

Fig. 2.40 Integrated RAM implementation of registers, stack, and data store

processor services individual input and output lines on the same input/output port and performs logical processing operations on I/O data right at the interface. A programmable interval timer and an event counter are implemented in the chip for ease of monitoring and controlling man–machine interfaces, printers, stepping motors, and the like. The processor need no longer wait in a loop for I/O devices with long operating delays since it can be interrupted by the timer/counter when it counts down to zero.

The capability of the basic microcomputer can be expanded by adding to the system external memory modules or device controllers, as needed, via the system bus. Highly specialized I/O requirements can be implemented by connecting programmable interfaces and device controllers to the system bus.

Microprocessor Testing

Since a microprocessor is at the heart of a microcomputer system, it may cause a total system failure if it does not perform according to specifications. However, faults in microprocessor chips are hard to detect for many reasons. First of all, failure modes of microprocessors are not well known among users. The data supplied by the manufacturers is usually inadequate for identifying probable conditions of failure since these may be very subtle and difficult to uncover. The timing diagrams in this chapter indicate that a transient error in the timing of one signal can cause a whole sequence of operations to fail. Because of the pin limitations on the chips, it is also impossible to monitor every operation inside them. Often the best that can be done is to observe the changes in the input and output signals while the microprocessor is executing a selected set of instructions. Finally, the testing system for a microprocessor must supply input signals and record output signals at speeds matching the speed of operation of the microprocessor. Often, this speed of operation is too high for conventional logic-circuit test devices.

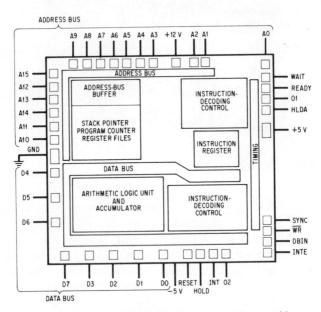

Fig. 2.41   Layout of elements in a microprocessor chip

It is not feasible to do an exhaustive test of a microprocessor chip for all possible combinations of data and instructions because of their immense number. Assuming that a single test can be performed in one microsecond, it has been estimated that an exhaustive test of an eight-bit microprocessor with ten instructions will take approximately 38 years. Therefore, the user should concentrate on testing with only "worst case" or "worst known" combinations of data and instructions. The only problem is that these are not well defined, well known, nor easily available.

Being programmable, a microprocessor can be considered to be a "smart" logic device; this attribute can be used advantageously for testing. The microprocessor chip is placed in its intended operating environment and exercised by a self-diagnosing test program supplied by the manufacturer in a ROM. Test systems similar in nature are supplied by many companies—for example, Micro Control Corp., Motorola Inc., and Rockwell. However, such systems are still expensive and may well be beyond the budget of a hobbyist. Test systems based on self-diagnostic programs have the following disadvantages: (1) Multiple faults may remain undetected; (2) long diagnostic programs may run to completion even with the early occurrence of a fault; (3) special hardware may be needed to test external conditions such as random occurrence of interrupts; and (4) faults may keep a microprocessor from executing a test.

In general, microprocessors can be tested in one of two ways. In the first approach, the chip is tested as a single system with specified input/output characteristics. The second approach treats the chip as a combination of functional components that are to be tested in some rea-

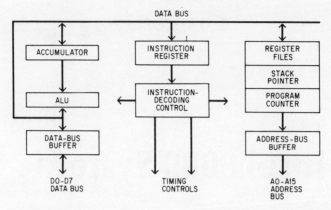

Fig. 2.42 A microprocessor as a collection of functional components

sonable sequence. The test input patterns may either be stored and re-trieved from memory or generated by executing special test algorithms. The physical layout of the elements in a microprocessor chip, an example of which is shown in Fig. 2.41, leads one to consider a chip as a collection of functional components, as shown in Fig. 2.42. A reasonable sequence of tests for testing such a collection is given in Table 2.5.

In conclusion, note that most testing systems for microprocessors now available are too expensive for the hobbyist. Only companies with product lines based on microprocessors can use them in a cost effective manner. However, in the future, reasonably priced test systems based on the approach discussed above may become available. Computer clubs may rent or purchase such equipment to be shared by their members.

Table 2.5 Testing Scheme of a Microprocessor Chip

Test sequence	Test Description
1. Reset	Reset microprocessor by means of the RESET input signal
2. Test program counter	Increment the program counter through its full range by means of the no-operation instruction
3. Test memory	Test the internal registers or on-chip RAM by means of test patterns
4. Test stack pointer	Increment and decrement the stack pointer through its full range
5. Test ALU	Test the ability of the ALU to add, subtract, detect a zero, positive, or negative value, set carry, and perform logic operations
6. Test accumulator	Test load, store, shift, rotate, and the like operations involving the accumulator
7. Timing and control	Test the responses to all external signals such as interrupts and requests for the exclusive use of bus
8. Test instruction decoder	Execute all other instructions not utilized so far

Chapter 3

Intel 8080 System

Introduction

Intel's 8080 microcomputer system is one of the earliest and most popular eight-bit systems available; it is a direct descendant of the older 8008 microprocessor. Figure 3.1 shows the microprocessor with its clock circuit and bus interface chips. It uses three levels of power supply ± 5 V and ± 12 V, and signals are TTL compatible. With a 500-ns clock period,

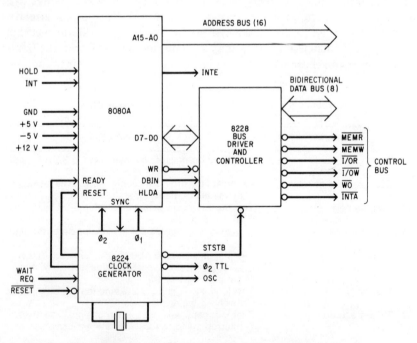

Fig. 3.1 The 8080 microprocessor system

an 8080A executes its instructions within 2 to 9 μs. Since the 8080A was designed during the early stages of microprocessor development, it has certain shortcomings. Despite these, it is popular—a reflection of the flexibility of its chip architecture.

One of the shortcomings of an 8080A is the lack of a clock circuit on the chip, requiring clock signals to be generated by a separate chip (8224). This was common practice with early versions of most microprocessors. Furthermore, since an 8080A microprocessor chip does not directly generate a set of control signals that is comprehensive enough to control all the peripheral support chips, a separate bus interface and control chip (8228) must be employed. These three chips and other support chips will be discussed in detail in the following sections.

8224 Clock Generator

The 8224 clock generator chip with its pin assignments and signal descriptions is shown in Fig. 3.2. Above and beyond generating the clock signals, it also provides some control signals for the 8080A and 8228 chips.

The primary signals out of 8224 are the two-phase signals, ϕ_1 and ϕ_2, which are controlled by a crystal oscillator connected between XTAL1 and XTAL2. As shown in Fig. 3.3, the clock signals are derived from the outputs of a divide-by-nine counter, and hence the period of the

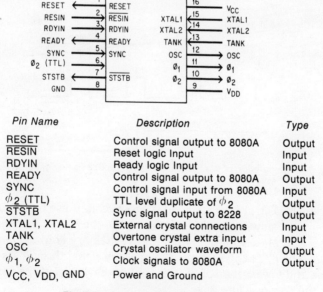

Pin Name	Description	Type
RESET	Control signal output to 8080A	Output
RESIN	Reset logic Input	Input
RDYIN	Ready logic Input	Input
READY	Control signal output to 8080A	Output
SYNC	Control signal input from 8080A	Input
ϕ_2 (TTL)	TTL level duplicate of ϕ_2	Output
STSTB	Sync signal output to 8228	Output
XTAL1, XTAL2	External crystal connections	Input
TANK	Overtone crystal extra input	Input
OSC	Crystal oscillator waveform	Output
ϕ_1, ϕ_2	Clock signals to 8080A	Output
V_{CC}, V_{DD}, GND	Power and Ground	

Fig. 3.2　An 8224 clock generator chip

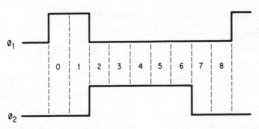

Fig. 3.3   Clock signals ϕ_1 and ϕ_2 for the 8080 system

crystal oscillator must be exactly one-ninth of the desired clock period. The most commonly used clock period of 500 ns thus requires an 18-MHz crystal. If an overtone mode of crystal is used, its supporting LC network must be connected to the TANK input of 8224. The clock generator outputs a TTL-compatible ϕ_2 signal—ϕ_2 (TTL)—for use by the other components of the system. The crystal oscillator frequency is also available at the OSC output line.

    The RESET output signal of the 8224 chip can be used to reset the 8080A microprocessor under such conditions as a power failure or a manual reset operation executed by a human operator. The input signal for such a reset operation is accepted by the 8224 on its $\overline{\text{RESIN}}$ input line. A Schmitt trigger within the 8224 creates a reset logic level with $\overline{\text{RESIN}}$ falls below a threshold value. As shown in Fig. 3.4, the 8224 chip samples this reset logic level during a ϕ_2 clock phase and generates a sharp RESET signal for the 8080A chip.

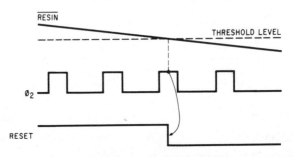

Fig. 3.4   Generation of the RESET signal by the 8224 clock generator chip

    The READY output signal of the 8224 chip is used by such system components as slow memory devices to force the 8080A microprocessor to enter a wait state where it waits for the memory chip to complete its operation. The 8224 chip accepts the memory signal through its RDYIN input line and lowers the READY output to the 8080A at the next occurrence of the ϕ_2 clock (see Fig. 3.5).

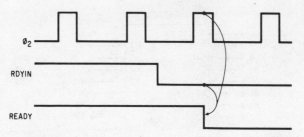

Fig. 3.5 Generation of the READY signal for the 8080A

The SYNC signal is sent to the 8224 chip by the 8080A to identify the first period of its machine cycle. In its turn, the 8224 chip uses SYNC to generate the $\overline{\text{STSTB}}$ signal for bus controller 8228, which reads in the status of the 8080A from the data bus. The uses of READY, SYNC, and $\overline{\text{STSTB}}$ are explained in more detail in later sections.

8080A Microprocessor

An 8080A microprocessor has seven 8-bit addressable registers, a 16-bit stack pointer, and a 16-bit program counter, as shown in Fig. 3.6. The A register is the primary accumulator; the six remaining 8-bit reg-

7		0	
	PSW		PROGRAM STATUS WORD
	A		PRIMARY ACCUMULATOR

15	8	7	0	
B		C		SECONDARY ACCUMULATORS/DATA COUNT
D		E		SECONDARY ACCUMULATORS/DATA COUNT
H		L		MAIN DATA COUNTER
SP				STACK POINTER
PC				PROGRAM COUNTER

Fig. 3.6 Addressable registers of an 8080A

isters (B, C, D, E, H, and L) are used either as secondary accumulators or as three (BC, DE, and HL) 16-bit data counters. The HL combination is normally used as a data counter for operand addressing. The stack pointer (SP) can be used to create a software controlled stack in memory. The 8-bit PSW register stores status information such as sign bit, carry bit, zero indicator bit, and the like, that result from the execution of certain instructions.

The 8080A chip with its pin assignments and signal descriptions is shown in Fig. 3.7. The sixteen address lines A0, . . . , A15 are used by an 8080A to address memory words and input/output devices. These are

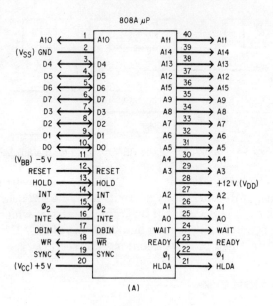

(A)

Pin Name	Description	Type
A0–A15	Address lines	Tristate, output
D0–D7	Data Bus lines	Tristate, bidirectional
SYNC	Machine Cycle Synchronizer	Output
DBIN	Data Input Strobe	Output
READY	Data Input Stable	Input
WAIT	CPU In Wait state	Output
$\overline{WR}$	Data Output Strobe	Output
HOLD	Enter Hold state	Input
HLDA	Hold Acknowledge	Output
INT	Interrupt Request	Input
INTE	Interrupt Enable	Output
RESET	Reset CPU	Input
ϕ_1, ϕ_2	Clock signals	Input
$V_{SS}, V_{DD}, V_{CC}, V_{BB}$	Power and Ground	

Fig. 3.7 (a) The 8080A microprocessor chip, and (b) functional block diagram of an 8080A microprocessor chip

tristate lines that may be floated, at which time support chips can use them without any interference from the 8080A. The eight data lines D0, . . . , D7 are used by an 8080A to transfer data with the support chips. The data lines are also used to transmit status information from the 8080A to the 8228 bus controller and buffer chip. Using this status information, the 8228 chip generates a comprehensive set of control signals for the 8080A. The data bus is thus shared by the data bytes and the status information. This status information is discussed in the next section, which describes the 8228 chip. Because of limitations on current that can be drawn from an 8080A, the support chips cannot be directly

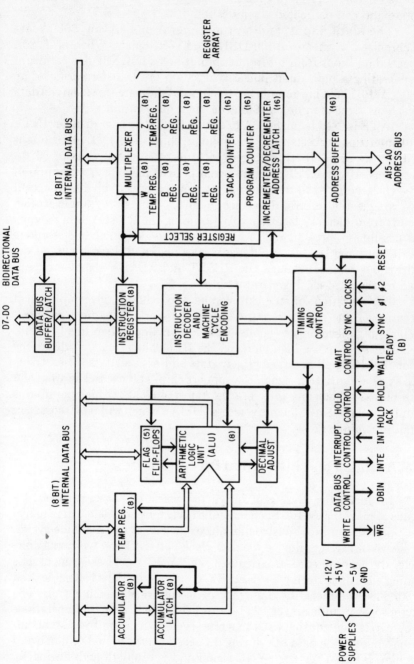

Fig. 3.7(b) Functional block diagram.

connected to the data bus of *the microprocessor chip;* instead, they are buffered by the 8228 chip. Like the address lines, the data lines are also tristate and can be floated when desired.

The data input and output operations of an 8080A are synchronized by means of the DBIN and $\overline{WR}$ signals. When an 8080A expects data input from a support chip, it holds DBIN high as a means of generating a data input pulse. When data are transferred out of an 8080A, $\overline{WR}$ is held low to indicate that output data are stable on the data lines. This signal can be used to generate a data output pulse.

INTE is used by an 8080A to enable (INTE = 1) or disable (INTE = 0) interrupt requests from the support chips. The INT input line is used by the external chips to request interrupts (INT = 1) of 8080A operations. If the RESET input signal is held high for a minimum of three clock periods, all the internal register contents of an 8080A except PSW are cleared to zero. Resetting an 8080A causes program execution to start from memory location 0. By lowering the READY input signal, it is possible to force an 8080A into a wait state. When an 8080A enters a wait state, the WAIT output signal goes high and the contents of the address bus remains stable. The RESET and READY signals are supplied by the 8224 clock generator chip.

The operations of an 8080A can be stopped after the completion of execution of one instruction and before the start of the next by introducing a high-level input signal on the HOLD line. When this happens, an 8080A sends out a high value on the HLDA line to acknowledge the input HOLD signal and floats the tristate address and data buses. Using HLDA as an initiation signal, the support chips can use the address and data buses without any interference from the 8080A. This operation is mainly used for direct memory access (DMA), which will be discussed in detail in Chap. 6.

8080A Timing and Instruction Execution

In an 8080A, timing of instruction execution is carried out by means of machine cycles. Each machine cycle may consist of three to five clock periods, and each instruction may take one to five machine cycles. As shown in Fig. 3.8, during the first clock period (T_0) of every machine cycle, the leading edge of ϕ_2 causes the SYNC signal to go high. The leading edge of ϕ_2 during T_1 resets SYNC; thus the SYNC signal is used by an 8080A to mark the first clock period of every machine cycle. The microprocessor informs the 8228 controller of the sequence of operations to be carried out during each machine cycle by transmitting status information over the data bus during the second clock period (T_1) of every machine cycle. When the SYNC signal and ϕ_1 are both high during T_1, the 8224 clock generator sends a status strobe signal $\overline{STSTB}$ to the 8228

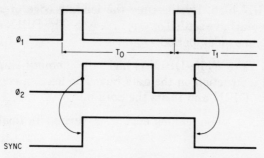

Fig. 3.8 Identifying clock period T₀ of every machine cycle by SYNC high

controller chip. The controller receives the status information from the data lines of the 8080A and —in conjunction with the three control signals DBIN, $\overline{WR}$, and HLDA—generates the necessary control signals for that machine cycle. The timing diagram of this sequence of events is shown in Fig. 3.9.

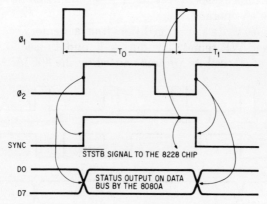

STSTB SIGNAL TO THE 8228 CHIP

STATUS OUTPUT ON DATA BUS BY THE 8080A

Fig. 3.9 Status output on data bus by an 8080A during T₀ of every machine cycle

Instruction Fetch Phase

The following sequence of events occur during an instruction fetch phase:

Clock period T₀:　　WAIT signal is low and $\overline{WR}$ is high. The leading edge of ϕ_2 sets SYNC high, transfers contents of PC to A0, . . . , A15, and sets the status bits on D0, . . . , D7.

Clock period T₁:　The controller 8228 reads the status bits off D0, . . . , D7 during ϕ_1 of T₁. The leading edge of ϕ_2 in T₁ resets SYNC and sets DBIN high. By the time the leading edge of ϕ_2 arrives, the address bits have settled on A0, . . . , A15. The DBIN signal remains high for one clock period.

Clock period T_2: While DBIN is high, the memory chip puts the addressed instruction on the data bus. The leading edge of ϕ_2 during T_2 resets DBIN and floats the data bus.

Clock period T_3: The leading edge of ϕ_2 during T_3 floats the address bus.

Memory Read and Write

As far as the support chips are concerned, a memory read operation is identical with an instruction fetch. However the status bits transmitted by the 8080A during a memory read is slightly different. The same timing diagram of Fig. 3.10 still applies to a memory read. Since memory is read during T_0, T_1, and T_2, memory reference instructions need two machine cycles to execute. The second machine cycle is used to fetch or store an operand.

A memory write operation differs from a memory read operation in that DBIN and $\overline{WR}$ remain low during T_1 and T_2 (see Fig. 3.11), and a different set of status bits are transmitted by the 8080A. An 8080A chip

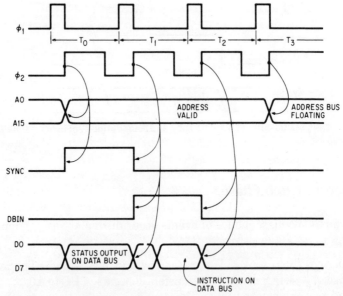

Fig. 3.10 Instruction fetch phase (during a normal fetch, as shown, READY and $\overline{WR}$ are high and WAIT is low)

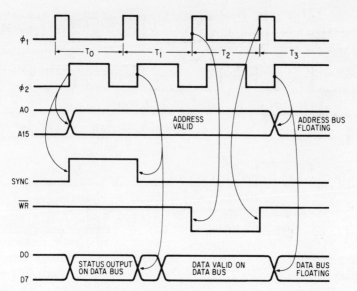

Fig. 3.11   Memory write operation (READY is high; $\overline{WR}$ and WAIT are low)

can access two different memory modules with overlapping addresses, and one of them can be organized as a last-in-first-out stack. This stack memory is addressable by the contents of stack pointer SP. The set of status bits transmitted by the 8080A chip in the stack address mode is different from those used in normal memory address mode. These status bits and their use are discussed in the next section on the 8228 controller.

Wait State

A wait state can be introduced between clock periods T_1 and T_2 of a memory read or write operation; it is used by memory chips that operate at slower speeds than the microprocessor. If the READY signal is low during ϕ_2 of T_1, an 8080A CPU will enter a wait state following T_1. The wait state may consist of any number of clock periods during which the microprocessor does nothing but maintain all signal levels. It also samples the READY signal during all subsequent ϕ_2 pulses until it goes high again. At the next ϕ_1, the 8080A leaves the wait state and proceeds with instruction execution. The timing diagram of a memory read with an intermediate wait state is shown in Fig. 3.12. The transitions from the normal state of execution to the wait state and back are shown in Fig. 3.13. When an 8080A is in the wait state, the output signal WAIT is held at a high value.

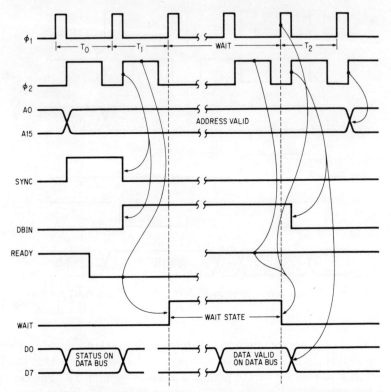

Fig. 3.12 Memory read operation with an intermediate WAIT state (WAIT is high in the WAIT state, which is initiated by lowering READY and terminated by resetting it)

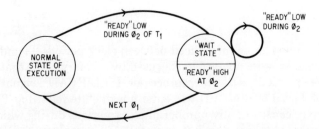

Fig. 3.13 Transitions to and from the wait state

Hold and Halt States

A hold state is initiated if some support chip sets the HOLD signal high. An 8080A acknowledges a hold request by setting HLDA high. If a hold is requested during a data input operation, then HLDA is set high by the leading edge of ϕ_1 in T_2. If hold is requested during a data output

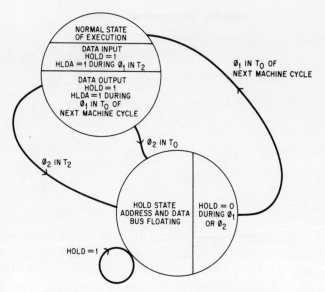

Fig. 3.14 Transitions to and from the hold state

operation, then HLDA is set high by the leading edge of ϕ_1 in the cycle following T_2. For a data input operation to be completed, data on the data bus must be valid until the leading edge of ϕ_2 in T_2, even after the HLDA is set high.

Setting HOLD low, which causes an exit from the hold state, must coincide with the leading edge of ϕ_1 or ϕ_2. The microprocessor will enter normal operation at ϕ_1 during T_0 of the next machine cycle and set HLDA low. The main difference between a hold state and a wait state is that during a hold state the data and address buses are floated and hence they can be used by the support chips without interference from the 8080A.

The halt state is entered by the execution of a halt instruction by the 8080A. In the halt state, the microprocessor does nothing but mark time, and the address and data buses are not floated. The only means of getting out of a halt state is an external interrupt signal. If the interrupt signal has been disabled before entering the halt state, then power to the system must be turned off and then turned on again.

During the halt state, the hold state may be entered by setting HOLD high, thus causing the data and the address buses to float. However, the halt state will be re-entered upon exit from the hold state. The hold and halt state transitions are shown in Figs. 3.14 and 3.15.

Reset Operation

The reset operation is initiated by setting the RESET signal high, which clears the contents of the program counter to zero and disables all

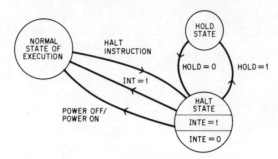

Fig. 3.15   Transitions to and from the halt state

interrupts. The RESET signal should be high for at least three clock periods. During the reset operation, the following sequence of operations is carried out: (1) The program counter is cleared, (2) all interrupts are disabled, (3) internal logic for INTE is reset, and (4) internal logic for HLDA is reset. When RESET becomes low, execution starts with the instruction at memory location 0 at the first ϕ_1 of the first clock period, but the interrupts remain disabled.

Interrupt Handling

External interrupts are handled by an 8080A by means of the INT and the INTE signals. When the microprocessor does not want to be interrupted, it sets INTE equal to 0. To enable external interrupts, an 8080A sets INTE equal to 1. The interrupt system can be enabled and disabled under program control by executing EI (enable) and DI (disable) instructions.

If INTE = 1, an external support chip can request an interrupt by setting INT equal to 1. An 8080A acknowledges an interrupt by setting INTE equal to 0 during the leading edge of ϕ_2 in the next T_0 clock period. At the same time, it transmits status bits to the 8228 controller, indicating the start of a post-interrupt instruction fetch. This interrupt initiation sequence is shown in Fig. 3.16.

The 8228 controller generates an interrupt acknowledge signal INTA for the interrupting device. A post-interrupt instruction fetch sequence is somewhat different from a normal instruction fetch. First of all, the contents of the program counter are not incremented. At this point, the program counter is still pointing at the next instruction of the interrupted program. The address of this instruction must be saved so that the interrupted program can restart execution after the interrupt has been serviced.

During the post-interrupt instruction fetch, an instruction is not fetched in the normal manner from the random-access memory. Rather

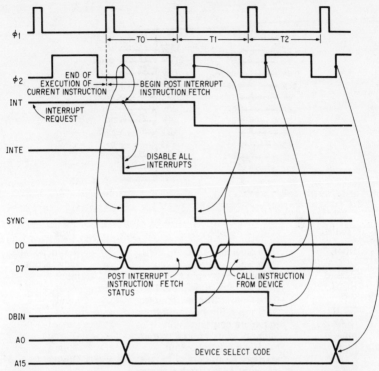

Fig. 3.16 Interrupt acknowledgment and post-interrupt instruction fetching

the 8080A fetches the object code of an instruction supplied by the interrupting device. Therefore, it is up to the interrupting device to supply a suitable instruction that causes the contents of the program counter to be saved. Usually, subroutine calls accomplish this, and, in the 8080 system, a subroutine can be called either by a CALL or a RSTn instruction. The interrupt service routine must end with a RETURN instruction, which restores the contents of the program counter to their pre-interrupt values in order to resume the execution of the interrupted program.

8228 Bus Controller

An 8080A microprocessor does not generate a comprehensive set of control signals to control its support chips. Instead, during T_0 it transmits a set of status bits to the external logic over D0, . . . , D7 data lines. The external logic circuit incorporates these status bits with DBIN, $\overline{\text{WR}}$, and HLDA to generate the necessary control signals. The support chips cannot be connected to an 8080A's data bus either; they must be buffered by external logic. An 8228 bus controller, whose pin assignments and signal

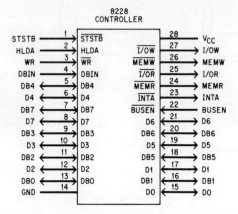

Fig. 3.17   An 8228 controller chip

descriptions are given in Fig. 3.17, performs these two functions of the external logic for an 8080A microprocessor.

The patterns of status bits transmitted to an 8228 controller by an 8080A microprocessor are shown in Table 3.1. The status bits output on the data bus have the following significance:

D0 (Interrupt Acknowledge):   D0 = 1 means generate interrupt acknowledge signal INTA. The interrupting device should use this signal to transfer a restart (RSTn) to the 8080A while DBIN is high.

$\overline{D1}$ *(Data Output):* $\overline{D1}$ = 1 indicates a data output operation from the 8080A to the memory, stack memory, or input/output device.

D2 (Stack Operation):   D2 = 1 indicates a read/write operation with stack memory. The address lines A0, . . . , A15 transmits the contents of stack pointer SP.

Table 3.1 Status Output from an 8080A

D7	D6	D5	D4	D3	D2	D1	D0	Operation
1	0	1	0	0	0	1	0	Instruction fetch
0	0	1	0	0	0	1	1	Interrupt acknowledge and fetch
1	0	0	0	0	0	1	0	Memory read
1	0	0	0	0	1	1	0	Stack read
0	1	0	0	0	0	1	0	Input from device
0	0	0	0	0	0	0	0	Memory write
0	0	0	0	0	1	0	0	Stack write
0	0	0	1	0	0	0	0	Output to device
1	0	0	0	1	0	1	0	Halt acknowledge
0	0	1	0	1	0	1	1	Interrupt acknowledge in halt state

D3 (Halt Acknowledge):   D3 = 1 generates an acknowledgement signal for the halt instruction.

D4 (Output to Device):   D4 = 1 indicates that the address bus is addressing an input/output device and data for the device will be available on the data bus when $\overline{WR}$ is low.

D5 (Instruction Fetch):   D5 = 1 indicates a fetch phase for the first byte of an instruction.

D6 (Input from Device):   D6 = 1 indicates that the address bus is addressing an input/output device and the data from device should be on the data bus when DBIN is high.

D7 (Memory Read):   D7 = 1 indicates that the 8080A is executing a memory read operation.

The output signals of an 8228 controller are, as follows: (1) $\overline{MEMR}$ —a read-memory pulse, (2) $\overline{MEMW}$—a write-memory pulse, (3) $\overline{IOR}$— a read-device pulse, (4) $\overline{IOW}$—a write-device pulse, and (5) $\overline{INTA}$—an interrupt acknowledge signal. Table 3.2 shows how these signals are generated from the status bits and the input signals from an 8080A.

Table 3.2 Output Signals of an 8228 Controller

D7	D6	D4	D0	DBIN	$\overline{WR}$	8228 Output
1	–	–	–	1	–	$\overline{MEMR}$ = 0
–	–	0	–	–	0	$\overline{MEMW}$ = 0
–	1	–	–	1	–	$\overline{IOR}$ = 0
–	–	1	–	–	0	$\overline{IOW}$ = 0
–	–	–	1	–	–	$\overline{INTA}$ = 0

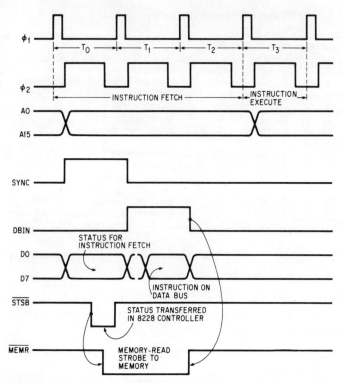

Fig. 3.18   Input and output signals of an 8228 controller during an instruction fetch

The status output on the data bus is transferred into the 8228 by the $\overline{STSTB}$ = 0 pulse generated by the 8224 clock generator. A timing diagram showing an instruction fetch and execution is given in Fig. 3.18.

8212 Parallel Input/Output Port

An 8212 is a simple but versatile parallel input/output port that can be extremely useful in a microcomputer system. Unlike the parallel input/output port discussed in Chap. 2, an 8212 cannot be programmed. However, the programmable input/output ports of the Intel 8080 family are somewhat difficult to program and operate. Normally, an 8212 provides enough parallel input/output capability for most hobby computers.

The pin assignments and signal descriptions of an 8212 are shown in Fig. 3.19. In order to understand the operating modes of this device, it is necessary to consider its internal logic circuit (see Fig. 3.20). This device stores eight bits of data in the eight D-flipflops shown in Fig. 3.20. The D-flipflops are not edge-triggered, that is, the Q outputs reflect the

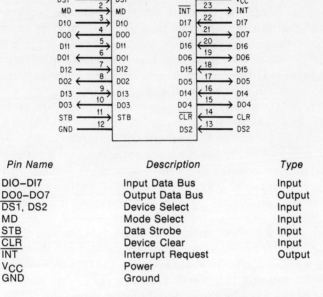

Fig. 3.19 An 8212 parallel input/output port

Pin Name	Description	Type
DIO–DI7	Input Data Bus	Input
DOO–DO7	Output Data Bus	Output
$\overline{DS1}$, DS2	Device Select	Input
MD	Mode Select	Input
STB	Data Strobe	Input
$\overline{CLR}$	Device Clear	Input
$\overline{INT}$	Interrupt Request	Output
V_CC	Power	
GND	Ground	

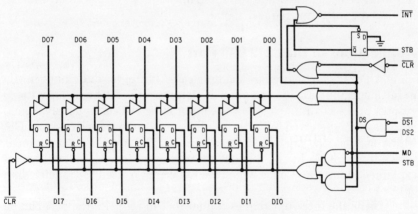

Fig. 3.20 Internal logic of an 8212 port

D input signals as long as the C input signal is high. When the C input goes low, the Q outputs latch onto the values of the D inputs. The Q outputs are connected to noninverting tristate buffers whose outputs are attached to the output lines. The device can be selected by using a low value for $\overline{DS1}$ and a high value for DS2, causing the device select signal DS to be high.

The operating mode of an 8212 is selected by the mode control signal MD. When MD is high, the tristate output buffers are permanently enabled, and therefore the Q outputs are permanently connected to the output lines. The input values are clocked into the D-flipflops by the device select signal DS. In this mode of operation, whenever the device select signal goes high, the data on the input lines is latched into the D-flipflops, making it available at the output lines. This mode of operation is known as the *output mode*.

When MD is low, the tristate output buffers are no longer permanently enabled. Moreover, the device select signal DS no longer acts as the clock signal for the D-flipflops, but the strobe signal STB can now be used as a clock signal and the input data is strobed into the D-flipflops by STB quite independently of the device select process. At this point, the device select signal DS enables the output buffers and the Q outputs appear on the output lines. This mode of operation is known as the *input mode*.

In the input mode, an 8212 transfers data from an external device to an 8080A. The trailing edge of the STB pulse clocks the service request flipflop, whose output is used to create an interrupt request signal ($\overline{INT}$). This signal informs the 8080A that data has been stored in the D-flipflops of the 8212 by the external device. When the 8080A acknowledges the interrupt request and selects the 8212 port (DS high), the output buffers are enabled and the interrupt request logic is reset, thus removing the interrupt request signal.

Applications of the 8212 I/O Port

An 8212 can be used as a simple gated buffer for data input if MD is set low (input mode) and STB is permanently set high. Now the Q outputs of the D-flipflops follow the input D signals continuously. The Q outputs are transferred to the output lines by the device select signal DS, which enables the tristate output buffers. This mode of operation is shown in Fig. 3.21. For simple data output operation, MD is set high, as explained before, and once again the DS signal is used to transfer data out.

Using the interrupt request signal $\overline{INT}$ of an 8212, the port can be used to transfer data according to the handshaking protocol described in Chap. 2. In the input mode, MD is set low, and data transfer proceeds as shown in Fig. 3.22. As shown in Fig. 3.23, the $\overline{DS1}$ signal is derived from the $\overline{IOR}$ of the 8228 bus controller, and the DS2 is obtained from decoding the address bits on the address bus. The external device strobes data into the 8212 using the STB signal. The role of the 8080A and the external device can be interchanged in Fig. 3.23, resulting in Fig. 3.24. Now the 8212 acts as an output port using the handshaking protocol. The

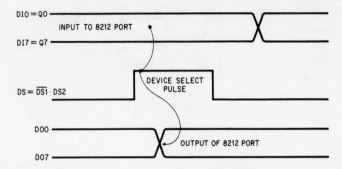

Fig. 3.21 An 8212 port as a simple gated buffer (MD, low; STB, high; DS used as input pulse)

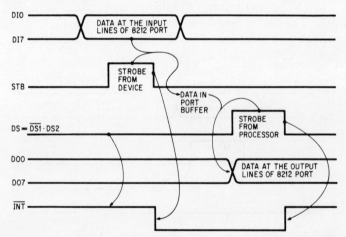

Fig. 3.22 Data input with handshaking (device uses STB to strobe data in port and generate interrupt request $\overline{INT}$; processor uses DS to strobe data out and reset $\overline{INT}$)

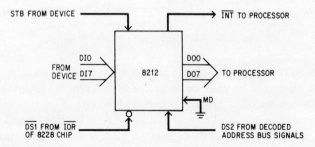

Fig. 3.23 An 8212 used for input with handshaking (timing diagram shown in Fig. 3.22)

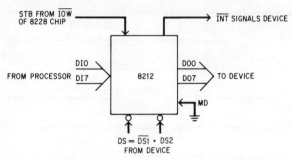

Fig. 3.24 An 8212 used for output with handshaking (timing diagram shown in Fig. 3.25)

8080A strobes data in the 8212 using the $\overline{\text{IOW}}$ signal of the 8228 controller. The $\overline{\text{INT}}$ signal informs the device that data is available in the 8212 buffer. The device uses the select signal ($\overline{\text{DS1}}$ and DS2) to read data from the 8212 and reset $\overline{\text{INT}}$. The timing diagram of such a transfer is shown in Fig. 3.25.

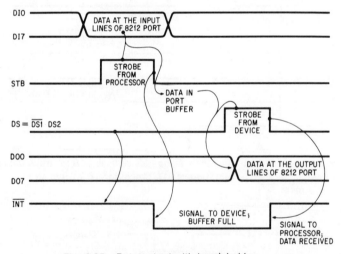

Fig. 3.25 Data output with handshaking

An 8212 port has various other applications as well. As shown in Fig. 3.26, they can be used by a device to transmit a restart instruction (RSTn) to an 8080A after the acknowledgement of its interrupt signal. The object code for RSTn is 1 1 1 X X X 1 1 where the Xs are bits selected by the device. In this case, the 8212 is acting as a simple gated buffer for data input to the 8080A. As shown in Chap. 6, 8212s can also be used as buffers between an analog-to-digital converter and a micro-

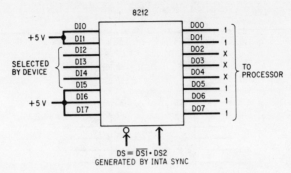

Fig. 3.26 An 8212 used to transmit a restart instruction, RST n, to processor after interrupt acknowledgment

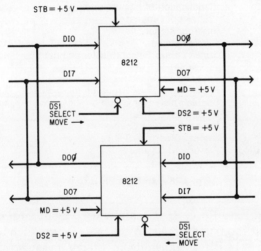

Fig. 3.27 Two 8212s are bidirectional bus drivers

processor. Finally, as shown in Fig. 3.27, they can also be used as bus drivers for bidirectional buses.

8214 Priority Interrupt Control Unit

If more than one peripheral device communicates with an 8080A by means of the interrupt signal INT, then it becomes necessary to arbitrate priorities among simultaneously occurring interrupt signals. A simple device to carry out this operation, quite sufficient for most home microprocessor systems, is the 8214 priority interrupt control unit (PICU). The pin assignments and signal descriptions of an 8214 PICU are shown in Fig. 3.28.

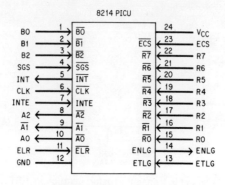

Pin Name	Description	Type
$\overline{R0}$–$\overline{R7}$	External Interrupt Request lines	Input
$\overline{A0}$–$\overline{A2}$	Identification of highest priority interrupt request	Output
$\overline{INT}$	Interrupt signal	Output
$\overline{B0}$–$\overline{B2}$	Current status	Input
SGS	Status Group Select (Master comparator disable)	Input
$\overline{ECS}$	Enable Current Status (Chip Select)	Input
ENLG	Enable Nest Level Group on daisy chain	Output
ETLG	Enable This Level Group on daisy chain	Input
$\overline{ELR}$	Enable Level Read	Input
INTE	Master Interrupt Enable	Input
$\overline{CLK}$	System Clock (ϕ_2 TTL)	Input
V_{CC}, GND	Power and Ground	

Fig. 3.28   An 8214 PICU chip

The input lines $\overline{R0}, \ldots, \overline{R7}$ can be used by at most eight devices to transmit their interrupt signals. When one or more such interrupt signals arrive, the 8214 PICU transmits an interrupt request signal $\overline{INT}$ to the 8080A microprocessor. The identification number of the highest priority incoming interrupt signal is transmitted over the output lines $\overline{A0}$, $\overline{A1}$, and $\overline{A2}$. The priorities of the incoming interrupt signals and their identification numbers in binary are listed in Table 3.3. The 8080A can unconditionally disable the 8214 PICU by setting the input signal INTE to low.

An 8214 PICU contains a programmable (write only) eight-bit register that can be used by the 8080A to disable this interrupt control device partially. When an 8214 is partially disabled, it ignores all interrupt requests of priority lower than a number specified by the 8080A. The microprocessor uses the $\overline{ECS}$ signal to select the programmable control register in the 8214 prior to writing control information in it. The four bits of the highest order of the control register are not used in the selective disable operation. If bit 3 is set to 1, all interrupts are enabled.

Table 3.3 Priority Assignments to $\overline{R7}$, ..., $\overline{R0}$ Listed in Decreasing Order of Priority

Priority Request Line	Identification Number			
	$\overline{A2}$	$\overline{A1}$	$\overline{A0}$	
$\overline{R7}$	1	1	1	Highest Priority
$\overline{R6}$	1	1	0	
$\overline{R5}$	1	0	1	
$\overline{R4}$	1	0	0	
$\overline{R3}$	0	1	1	
$\overline{R2}$	0	1	0	
$\overline{R1}$	0	0	1	
$\overline{R0}$	0	0	0	Lowest Priority

Therefore, in order to disable the interrupts selectively, bit 3 is normally set to zero. If bits 2, 1, and 0 are all set to zeros, all interrupts are disabled. If the decimal value of the number stored in bits 2, 1, and 0 is N ($7 \geq N > 0$), then only those interrupt requests in the range $\overline{R7}$ to $\overline{R}$ (8- N) inclusive are enabled.

In situations where more than eight interrupt request signals must be handled, several 8214 PICUs can be cascaded together to do the job. Each 8214 chip has an ETLG input line and an ENLG output line. To cascade these chips, the ENLG line of one chip is connected to the ETLG line of the next lower chip in the cascade. The ETLG line of the highest priority 8214 chip is connected to the power supply. If this chip has no interrupt request pending on its $\overline{R0}$, ..., $\overline{R7}$ lines, it raises its ENLG output signal, thus enabling the next 8214 chip in the cascade. The first chip in the cascade with one or more pending interrupt requests lowers the ENLG signal, thereby disabling all the 8214 chips under it in the cascade.

An 8214 PICU has no output lines to inform an interrupting device that its interrupt has been acknowledged. The interrupting device must use the A0, A1, A2 lines and the $\overline{INTA}$ line from the 8228 controller to determine when its interrupt is acknowledged. Until such time, it must maintain its interrupt request signal at the input of the PICU. Furthermore, upon acknowledgement of its interrupt, the device must remove its interrupt request signal from the PICU input.

A possible arrangement for handling interrupts from devices using an 8214 PICU and an 8212 I/O PORT is shown in Fig. 3.29. Here the 8212 port is used to transmit a restart instruction (RSTn) to the 8080A (see Fig. 3.26). The object code of an RSTn instruction is 1 1 1 X X X 1 1; the X bits are selected by output lines $\overline{A0}$, $\overline{A1}$, and $\overline{A2}$, which identify the device whose interrupt request is sent to the 8080A by the 8214 PICU. The $\overline{INTA}$ signal from the 8228 bus controller is used to select the 8212 output for the 8080A.

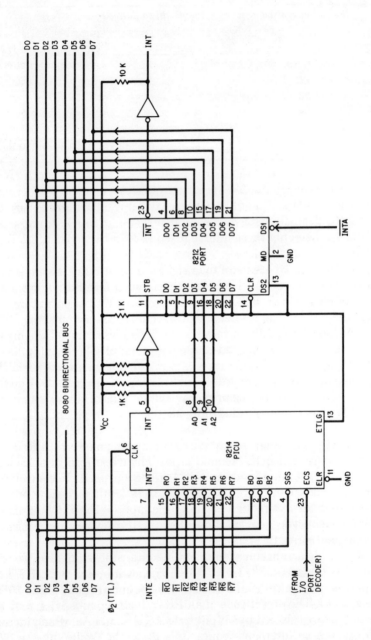

Fig. 3.29   Multiple interrupt handling using a PICU and an 8212 port

μPD369 Universal Asynchronous Receiver and Transmitter

A microcomputer interfaces with many devices, such as teletypes and cassette units, that transfer data in an asynchronous bit serial mode. In the serial mode, data bytes are transferred one bit at a time. In the asynchronous mode, the transmitter maintains a high mark signal when no data is transmitted, starts every data transmission with a start bit, and ends every transmission with one or two stop bits. This mode of transmission was discussed in Chap. 2. The input/output ports for managing such data transfers are called *UARTs* (Universal Asynchronous Receiver and Transmitter). A simple UART, the μPD369 manufactured by NEC Microcomputer for the 8080 microcomputer system, will be described here since the usual programmable serial input/output port for the 8080 family supplied by INTEL is difficult to operate. The μPD369, which is functionally equivalent to the industry standard 1602 UART manufactured by Western Digital, is more than adequate for most hobby computer systems.

The pin assignments and signal descriptions of μPD369 are shown in Fig. 3.30. Such a UART can be divided into a transmitter section and a receiver section; each section can operate independently of the other.

The transmitter section of the μPD369 is double buffered, as shown in Fig. 3.31. The transmit buffer O2 contains the bit string which is transmitted out serially via the TRO line. The signal TRE remains high as long as buffer O2 is waiting for transfer of data from buffer O1 after the completion of a transmission. Buffer O1 receives data from the microprocessor's data bus. THRE remains high as long as O1 is waiting for data input. THRL is used to transfer data from the data bus into O1. The receiver section of μPD369, shown in Fig. 3.32, is also double buffered. Data is received serially via the RI line and assembled in I1. The signal DR goes high when assembled data is transferred from buffer I1 to I2 and remains high. RRD is used to transfer data from I2 to the data bus of the microcomputer. Then $\overline{DRR}$ is set low to reset DR to low. Timing diagrams are shown in Figs. 3.33 and 3.34.

The format of data for serial transmission is selected by the signals PI, EPE, SBS, WLS1, and WLS2. If the format is fixed, these signals can be set permanently. Otherwise, their values are obtained from the data bus, and the signal CRL is used to strobe these values in. PI = 0 adds a parity bit to the data being transmitted. The parity bit is omitted if PI = 1. When the parity bit is added, EPI = 0 selects odd parity and EPI = 1 results in even parity. SBS = 1 adds two stop bits; otherwise, only one stop bit is added. WLS1 and WLS2 select the number of data bits to be transmitted in accordance with the code shown in Table 3.4.

Errors in transmission, such as parity errors, framing errors, or overrun errors are detected by the receiver section. These error condi-

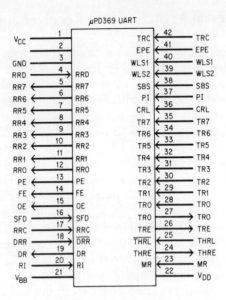

Pin Name	Description	Type
RR0–RR7	Parallel Received data output	Output
TR0–TR7	Parallel Transmitted data input	Input
MR	Master Reset	Input
TRO	Serial Data Output	Output
TRC	Transmit Clock	Input
PI	Parity Inhibit	Input
SBS	Stop Bits Select	Input
WLS1, WLS2	Word Length Select	Input
EPE	Odd/Even Parity select	Input
CRL	Control Load	Input —
TRE	Transmit Register Empty	Output
THRE	Transmit Holding Register Empty	Output
THRL	Transmit Holding Register Load	Input
RI	Serial Data Input	Input
RRC	Receiver Clock	Input
PE	Parity Error	Output
FE	Framing Error	Output
OE	Overrun Error	Output
SFD	Status Flag Disconnect	Input
DR	Data Received	Output
DRR	Data Received Reset	Input
RRD	Parallel Data Read Strobe	Input
V_{BB}, V_{CC}, V_{DD}, GND	Power and Ground	

Fig. 3.30 μPD369 UART chip

tions are identified by the PE, FE, and OE output signals. By setting SFD low, these error condition bits can be transferred from the chip to the microprocessor via the data bus. The transmitter and the receiver clock signals are supplied via the TRC and the RRC lines. These clocks

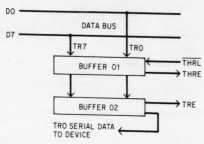

Fig. 3.31 The transmitter section of a μPD369 UART

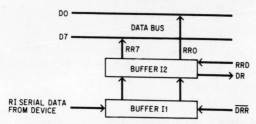

Fig. 3.32 The receiver section of a μPD369 UART

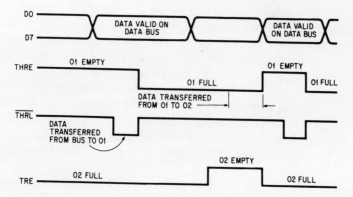

Fig. 3.33 Serial data output from a μPD369 UART (THRE can be used to generate an interrupt request and thus implement a handshaking protocol)

Table 3.4 Serial Transmission Data Bit Code

WLS2	WLS1	Number of data bits transmitted
0	0	5
0	1	6
1	0	7
1	1	8

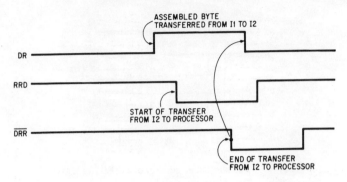

Fig. 3.34 Serial data input to a μPD369 UART (DR can be used to generate an interrupt request)

assist the transmitter and the receiver to pulse each bit being transferred, at the midpoint of its duration. The frequency of the clock must be 16 times the transmission frequency.

8253 Programmable Counter/Timer

The programmable counter/timer 8253 of Intel's 8080 family contains three independent programmable timing circuits. Each circuit can be operated as an interval timer, an event counter, or a periodic signal generator and a one-shot. The basic principle of operation of the programmable timer was discussed in Chap. 2. The pin assignments and signal descriptions of an 8253 chip are shown in Fig. 3.35.

Each timer uses a 16-bit counter and three associated signals. The 8253 chip is selected by the 8080A by means of the chip select signal $\overline{CS}$. As long as $\overline{CS} = 1$, the chip is not selected; selection takes place by lowering $\overline{CS}$. The signals A0 and A1 are used to address one of the three timing circuits or a control register. The codes for this selection are shown in Table 3.5.

Once a timer or the control register in an 8253 is selected by the 8080A, it can either read or write information in it from the data bus using the $\overline{RD}$ (read) and $\overline{WR}$ (write) control signals. If an 8253 is accessed as an input/output port, then $\overline{RD}$ and $\overline{WR}$ are connected to the $\overline{IOR}$ and $\overline{IOW}$ output signals of the 8228 bus controller. On the other

Table 3.5 Timer Code

A1	A0	
0	0	Select timer #0
0	1	Select timer #1
1	0	Select timer #2
1	1	Select control register

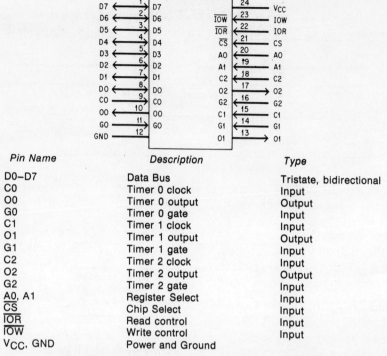

Pin Name	Description	Type
D0–D7	Data Bus	Tristate, bidirectional
C0	Timer 0 clock	Input
O0	Timer 0 output	Output
G0	Timer 0 gate	Input
C1	Timer 1 clock	Input
O1	Timer 1 output	Output
G1	Timer 1 gate	Input
C2	Timer 2 clock	Input
O2	Timer 2 output	Output
G2	Timer 2 gate	Input
A0, A1	Register Select	Input
$\overline{CS}$	Chip Select	Input
$\overline{IOR}$	Read control	Input
$\overline{IOW}$	Write control	Input
V$_{CC}$, GND	Power and Ground	

Fig. 3.35 An 8253 programmable counter/timer chip

hand, if it is accessed as part of memory (memory mapped I/O), then $\overline{RD}$ and $\overline{WR}$ are connected to the $\overline{MEMR}$ and $\overline{MEMW}$ signals, respectively.

The information read into the control register from the data bus controls the mode of operation, the method of counting, and the sequence of byte transfers involving the 16-bit counter. It should be emphasized that each of the three timers operates quite independently of the other two and can be individually controlled. The eight-bit control register format is discussed below. BO = 0 implies that the counter contents are binary numbers. BO = 1 implies that the counter contents are binary coded decimal (BCD) numbers. The modes of operation are selected by the bits B1, B2, and B3, as follows:

B3	B2	B1	
0	0	0	Mode 0
0	0	1	Mode 1
X	1	0	Mode 2
X	1	1	Mode 3
1	0	0	Mode 4
1	0	1	Mode 5

Bits B4 and B5 are used to specify the nature of the data transfer operations when the timers are being monitored by the 8080A, as follows:

B5	B4	
0	0	Latch counter value into register
0	1	Select low-order byte
1	0	Select high-order byte
1	1	Access low-order byte followed by high-order byte

Bits B6 and B7 are used to select the timer whose mode of operation is being set, as follows:

B7	B6	
0	0	Select timer #0
0	1	Select timer #1
1	0	Select timer #2

In the absence of any specific setting of these bits, zeros are assumed by default.

Each of the three timers has an input signal C, an output signal O, and a control (gate) signal G. The trailing edge of a pulse on C causes the counter to decrement its contents. If C is a periodic clock signal, then the timer acts as an interval timer. If C is aperiodic and is generated every time some outside event occurs, the timer acts as an event counter. An output signal is generated whenever the counter contents reach zero.

Modes of Operation of the Timer

Mode 0 When the control register is used to select one of the three timers and set it up for mode 0 operation, the output signal of the timer is set to zero. After the mode is set, an initial value is loaded into the 16-bit counter of the selected timer. The type of data transfer involved at this step is specified by bits B4 and B5 of the control register. After this data transfer operation is complete, the counter starts to decrement at every trailing edge of the C input signal. When the counter contents reach zero, the output signal goes high and stays high until it is reset.

In mode 0, the counter contents can be read or reset to a new starting value any time, even when the counter is active. The value read may decrement, however, while it is being read. The basic timing diagram in mode 0 is given in Fig. 3.36.

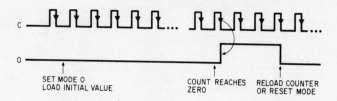

SET MODE 0
LOAD INITIAL VALUE

COUNT REACHES
ZERO

RELOAD COUNTER
OR RESET MODE

Fig. 3.36 Basic mode 0 operation of the programmable counter/timer

Mode 1 In this mode of operation, the counter does not start to decrement right after it is loaded. The process of decrementation is started by the leading edge of a pulse on control line G. Whenever a pulse occurs on G, the counter is reset to its initial value and the counting starts all over again, provided that the counter contents have not already reached zero. Reloading the counter with a new starting value while it is counting down has no effect on the counting process until the next pulse occurs on G. At the next pulse on G, the counter is reset to the new starting value. The timing diagrams of mode 1 operation are shown in Fig. 3.37.

Mode 2 In this mode, the counting process is repeated in a cyclic pattern. Normally, the output signal is high. When the counter contents reach zero, the output signal is set low and stays low for the duration of one clock pulse. Then the counter is automatically reinitiated, and the counting process starts all over. If the counter is reloaded with a new starting value, this new value is used to load the counter at the start of the next count cycle. The control signal G is used to trigger a new count cycle any time and can be used to synchronize the count cycle to some external event. Figure 3.38 shows the timing of events in this mode of operation.

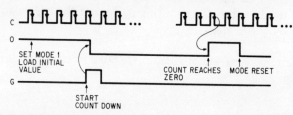

SET MODE 1
LOAD INITIAL
VALUE

COUNT REACHES
ZERO

MODE RESET

START
COUNT DOWN

Fig. 3.37 Basic mode 1 operation of the programmable counter/timer

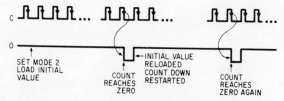

SET MODE 2
LOAD INITIAL
VALUE

COUNT
REACHES
ZERO

INITIAL VALUE
RELOADED
COUNT DOWN
RESTARTED

COUNT
REACHES
ZERO AGAIN

Fig. 3.38 Basic mode 2 operation of the programmable counter/timer

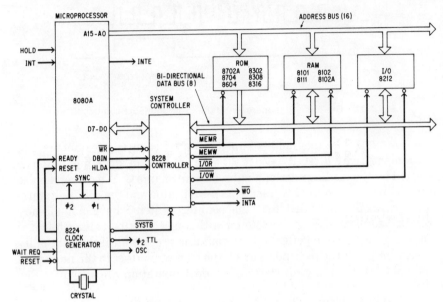

Fig. 3.39   A complete 8080 microcomputer system

Mode 3   In this mode, the counting process is repeated in a cyclic pattern as in mode 2. However, the output signal remains high for half the duration of the count cycle and remains low for the other half.

Mode 4   This mode of operation is similar to mode 2 except that the count cycle starts as soon as the second byte is loaded into the counter. The signal G cannot be used to start the count cycle. When G is low, the counter is disabled.

Mode 5   This mode is also very similar to mode 2. The trailing edge of G is used to start the counting cycle, but the cycle can no longer be disabled by the G signal.

A functional diagram of a complete 8080 microcomputer system is shown in Fig. 3.39.

Chapter 4

Zilog Z-80 System

Introduction

The Z-80 microprocessor and its support devices are manufactured by ZILOG Inc. This microprocessor was planned as an enhancement of Intel's 8080A by the same designers who designed the 8080A. It is necessary to have a clear idea of what this enhancement entails so as to avoid design errors in replacing an 8080A system with a Z-80. First of all, a Z-80 and an 8080A are not pin compatible, that is, it is not possible to replace an 8080A with a Z-80 without some hardware alterations. Since the instruction set of an 8080A, however, is a subset of the instruction set of Z-80, programs written for an 8080A can be executed on a Z-80. ROMs used with an 8080A can also be used with a Z-80. Program compatibility is really the most important aspect of any system enhancement since software is much more expensive than hardware. Furthermore, most 8080A support devices will also work with a Z-80.

In the Z-80 system, the three power supplies of an 8080A have been replaced by a single +5 V supply. The more complex two-phase clock (ϕ_1, ϕ_2) of an 8080A is replaced by a simple single-phase clock (ϕ). All of the 8224 clock generation circuitry is built into a Z-80 microprocessor chip. Similarly, the 8228 bus controller and buffer are integral parts of the Z-80 microprocessor chip as well. Hence, in contrast with Intel's three-chip 8080 system (see Fig. 3.1), the Z-80 is a single-chip microprocessor. A Z-80 also provides automatic dynamic memory refresh logic on the microprocessor chip; this can be very useful with the cheaper dynamic RAM chips.

The read and write control signals of the Z-80 are quite different from those of an 8080A. An 8080A uses an 8228 controller to generate four separate signals for memory read ($\overline{\text{MEMR}}$), memory write ($\overline{\text{MEMW}}$), input/output read ($\overline{\text{IOR}}$), and input/output write ($\overline{\text{IOW}}$). In contrast, a Z-80 microprocessor uses two general read and write signals

81

($\overline{\text{RD}}$ and $\overline{\text{WR}}$) in combination with a memory select ($\overline{\text{MREQ}}$) and input/output device select ($\overline{\text{IORQ}}$) signals. In addition to the standard $\overline{\text{RESET}}$ and $\overline{\text{INT}}$ signals, a Z-80 also uses a nonmaskable interrupt request signal $\overline{\text{NMI}}$. This signal is typically used to warn of an impending power failure so that a Z-80 can execute a special program to forestall it.

The instruction set of a Z-80 provides a block move instruction that can be used to move a block of data within the memory or from memory to an input/output port. A block of data can also be scanned for a specific value or character by executing a single instruction. Various other singular features of a Z-80 microprocessor will be discussed in the following sections.

Z-80 Microprocessor

A Z-80 microprocessor has two sets of seven eight-bit addressable registers and PSWs, as shown in Fig. 4.1. Each of these sets is identical to a similar set of registers in an 8080A (see Fig. 3.6). In addition, a Z-80 has a 16-bit program counter, a stack pointer, an index register, an eight-bit interrupt vector register, and a memory refresh counter. The stack pointer and program counter are identical to those available in an 8080A.

The presence of two sets of addressable registers, accumulators, and PSWs makes it easier for a Z-80 to handle single-level interrupts compared to an 8080A. To service a single interrupt, a Z-80 does not have to save the register contents on a stack but simply switches to the alternative register set. Only one of these two sets of registers, however, can be used at any given time.

The 16-bit index register allows the programmer more flexibility in addressing than is possible with an 8080A system. The interrupt vector register provides a Z-80 with the capability of supporting vectored interrupts. When one of these interrupts occurs, the interrupting device pro-

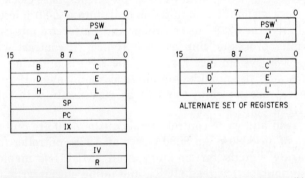

Fig. 4.1   Addressable register sets of a Z-80 (IX: index register; IV: interrupt vector register; R: refresh counter)

vides the lower byte of the address of the first instruction of an interrupt service routine. The upper byte of the two-byte address of the instruction is obtained from the interrupt vector register.

The built-in memory refresh counter makes it simpler to use a dynamic RAM with a Z-80 microprocessor. In a *dynamic RAM,* information bits are stored as electrical charges across capacitors that tend to leak and lose charge in a few milliseconds. Such dynamic memory elements require a refresh operation every few milliseconds to restore the original levels of the electrical charges. Dynamic RAMs have built-in refresh circuitry, but they need a counter to keep track of the sequence in which the words are refreshed. The memory refresh counter of the Z-80 microprocessor serves this purpose.

As mentioned before, the instruction set of an 8080A is a subset of the instruction set of a Z-80, that is, a Z-80 has all the instruction of an 8080A plus others. However, the operation codes of 8080A instructions use up almost all the possible bit patterns of an eight-bit byte. Thus, a Z-80 is forced to use some 16-bit operation codes, that is, some of the new instructions in the Z-80 instruction set use two eight-bit bytes for their operation codes.

A Z-80 microprocessor chip with its pin assignments and signal descriptions is shown in Fig. 4.2. The sixteen address lines A0, . . ., A15 are used to address memory words and input/output devices. Similar to the address lines of the 8080A, these are tristate lines and may be floated, at which time they can be used by support chips without interfering with the microprocessor. The eight data lines D0, . . . , D7 are used to transfer data; these, too, are tristate lines. Since a Z-80 does not output status signals for an external controller, it has no need to multiplex its data bus between data and status information.

The instruction fetch phase of a machine cycle is indicated by lowering the $\overline{\text{MI}}$ output signal. During an operand fetch from the memory, $\overline{\text{MI}}$ remains high. $\overline{\text{MREQ}}$ is lowered to identify any operation involving a memory access (read or write). Similarly, $\overline{\text{IORQ}}$ is lowered to indicate an input/output operation. When $\overline{\text{MREQ}}$ is low, the address on the address lines is interpreted as the address of a word in memory. On the other hand, when $\overline{\text{IORQ}}$ is low, the same address is interpreted as an input/output device select number.

The nature of a data transfer operation is identified by the $\overline{\text{RD}}$ and $\overline{\text{WR}}$ signals. When $\overline{\text{RD}}$ is low, a data read operation is in progress, and data is transferred into the microprocessor over the data bus. $\overline{\text{WR}}$ low identifies a data write operation, and data is transferred out of the microprocessor over the data bus. A low value of the $\overline{\text{RFSH}}$ signal identifies a memory refresh operation for a dynamic RAM. During a refresh operation, $\overline{\text{MREQ}}$ is also output low, and the address on the address lines is used to select the word in memory to be refreshed.

$\overline{\text{NMI}}$ is the highest priority, nonmaskable interrupt request signal. It is used to interrupt the microprocessor in case of an emergency such as a power failure. $\overline{\text{INT}}$ is the standard interrupt request signal from the input/output devices. The $\overline{\text{WAIT}}$ input signal of a Z-80 is equivalent to the READY signal of an 8080A. When $\overline{\text{WAIT}}$ is held low by the external logic, the microprocessor enters a wait state in which it marks time for the external logic to complete whatever operations are requested of it.

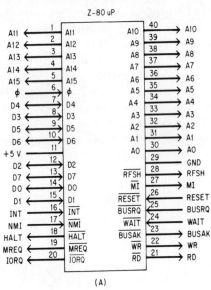

(A)

Pin Name	Description	Type
AO–A15	Address Bus	Tristate, output
DO–D7	Data Bus	Tristate, bidirectional
$\overline{\text{M1}}$	Identifies instruction fetch machine cycle	Output
$\overline{\text{MREQ}}$	Memory Request—indicates that CPU is performing memory access	Tristate, output
$\overline{\text{IORQ}}$	I/O Request—indicates I/O operation in progress	tristate, output
$\overline{\text{RD}}$	CPU read from memory or I/O device	Tristate, output
$\overline{\text{WR}}$	CPU write to memory or I/O device	Tristate, output
$\overline{\text{RFSH}}$	Refresh dynamic memories	Output
$\overline{\text{HALT}}$	CPU Halt executed	Output
$\overline{\text{WAIT}}$	Wait state request	Input
$\overline{\text{INT}}$	Interrupt request	Input
$\overline{\text{NMI}}$	Nonmaskable Interrupt request	Input
$\overline{\text{RESET}}$	Reset and initialize CPU	Input
BUSRQ	Request for control of address, data and control busses	Input
$\overline{\text{BUSAK}}$	Bus Acknowledge	Output
ϕ	CPU clock	Input
+5V, GND	Power and Ground	

Fig. 4.2   (a) Z-80 microprocessor chip

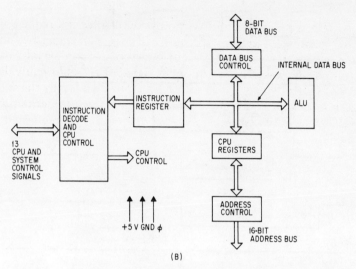

Fig. 4.2 (b) Functional block diagram of a Z-80 microprocessor chip

Unlike an 8080A, a Z-80 does not have an output signal to inform external logic that it is in the wait state. The $\overline{\text{RESET}}$ signal is used to reinitialize the microprocessor operations. When $\overline{\text{RESET}}$ is low, the contents of the program counter, interrupt vector, and the memory refresh counter are cleared to zeros. All interrupt requests, except the nonmaskable one, are disabled, and the tristate buses are floated. When the $\overline{\text{RESET}}$ signal is removed, operation starts with the instruction located at address zero.

The $\overline{\text{BUSRQ}}$ and $\overline{\text{BUSAK}}$ signals of a Z-80 are functionally equivalent to the HOLD nand HLDA signals of an 8080A. External logic can request exclusive use of the address and data buses by lowering $\overline{\text{BUSRQ}}$ input signal to the Z-80 microprocessor. The microprocessor floats the tristate buses and acknowledges the request by lowering $\overline{\text{BUSAK}}$. This exclusive use of buses by external logic is mainly needed for direct memory access (DMA) operation, which will be discussed in detail in Chap. 6.

Z-80 Timing and Instruction Execution

The clock periods and machine cycles of a Z-80 are much simpler than those of an 8080A. All machine cycles of a Z-80 consist of either three or four clock periods. In some cases, one or two clock periods in the wait state are automatically added to a machine cycle to allow external logic to complete the requested operations. Z-80 instructions need one to six machine cycles to complete execution.

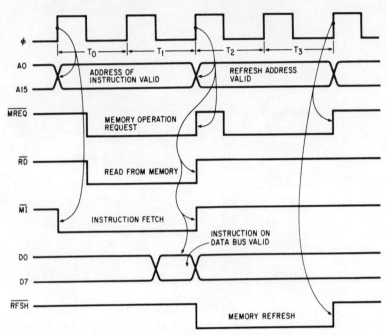

Fig. 4.3 Timing diagram of an instruction fetch operation

Instruction Fetch Phase

The following events occur during an instruction fetch phase:

Clock period T_0: The leading edge of clock pulse ϕ transfers the contents of the PC to A0, . . . , A15 and lowers $\overline{\text{MI}}$. A low value of $\overline{\text{MI}}$ identifies an instruction fetch operation and $\overline{\text{MI}}$ remains low throughout the fetch phase. Halfway through T_0, $\overline{\text{MREQ}}$ and $\overline{\text{RD}}$ are both lowered since this is a memory read operation. These two signals can be used to select a memory chip and read an instruction out.

Clock period T_1: The Z-80 waits for the instruction put on the data bus to settle.

Clock period T_2: The leading edge of ϕ in T_2 transfers the instruction from the data bus into the microprocessor. It also resets $\overline{\text{MI}}$, $\overline{\text{MREQ}}$, and $\overline{\text{RD}}$ and outputs the contents of the memory refresh counter onto A0, . . . , A15. The microprocessor spends T_2 and T_3 carrying out internal operations such as instruction transfer to IR and instruction decode.

Refresh operation: During T_2, $\overline{\text{MREQ}}$ and $\overline{\text{RFSH}}$ are set to low, indicating the start of a memory refresh operation. This operation

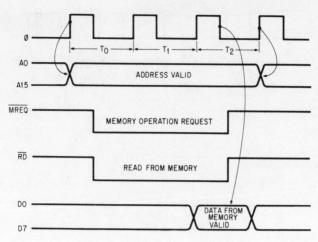

Fig. 4.4 Memory read operation

lasts until the end of T_3. The leading edge of ϕ at the end of T_3 resets $\overline{\text{RFSH}}$ and $\overline{\text{MREQ}}$, indicating the end of the memory refresh operation.

The timing diagram of this sequence of events is shown in Fig. 4.3.

Memory Read and Write

As far as an external memory chip is concerned, a memory read operation is the same as an instruction fetch operation. However, the timing of signals is somewhat different from the viewpoint of a Z-80 microprocessor. The timing diagram of a memory read operation is shown in Fig. 4.4. The address of the memory word is transferred to the address bus by the leading edge of ϕ during T_0. Halfway through T_0, $\overline{\text{MREQ}}$ and $\overline{\text{RD}}$ are lowered. $\overline{\text{MI}}$ remains high since this is not an instruction fetch. Then data is strobed into the microprocessor not by the leading edge, but by the trailing edge of ϕ in T_2. $\overline{\text{MREQ}}$ and $\overline{\text{RD}}$ are reset after the trailing edge of ϕ in T_2 has passed, and a new address is output by the leading edge of ϕ in the next period. Thus, a normal memory read operation takes only three clock periods, whereas an instruction fetch requires four.

The timing diagram of a memory write operation is shown in Fig. 4.5, and the sequence of events should be self-explanatory.

Wait State

A wait state can be introduced between clock periods T_1 and T_2 of a memory read or write operation, it is used by memory chips that oper-

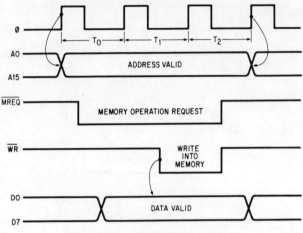

Fig. 4.5   Memory write operation

ate at slower speeds than the microprocessor. A Z-80 samples the $\overline{\text{WAIT}}$ input signal at the trailing edge of ϕ in T_1. If $\overline{\text{WAIT}}$ is low at that time, it enters a wait state and such a wait state may last for any number of clock periods during which the Z-80 does nothing but maintain all output signals. As soon as $\overline{\text{WAIT}}$ is found to be high on the trailing edge of a clock pulse, the Z-80 initiates the period T_2 with the next leading edge of ϕ. Note that a Z-80, unlike an 8080A, does not output any signal to inform external logic that it is in the wait state. The timing diagram of a memory read with a wait state lasting for two clock periods is shown in Fig. 4.6.

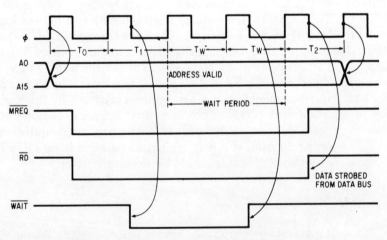

Fig. 4.6   Memory read operation with a wait period

Input and Output Operations

During data transfer operations with the input/output devices, a Z-80 uses $\overline{\text{IORQ}}$ instead of $\overline{\text{MREQ}}$. However, $\overline{\text{IORQ}}$ and $\overline{\text{RD}}$ or $\overline{\text{WR}}$ are lowered during the T_1 period rather than halfway into the T_0 period in order to provide the address on the address bus enough time to propagate to the input/output devices and be decoded.

A Z-80 also recognizes that input/output operations are inherently slower than other microprocessor operations. Hence, a wait state lasting for one clock period is automatically added in an input/output operation. Of course, the input/output devices can force the wait state to last longer, if necessary, by making use of the $\overline{\text{WAIT}}$ signal. The timing diagram of a normal input operation is shown in Fig. 4.7.

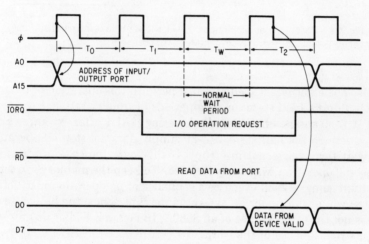

Fig. 4.7 Data input with a normal wait period

Hold and Halt States

The hold state for a Z-80 is initiated by the lowering of the $\overline{\text{BUSRQ}}$ signal. A Z-80 microprocessor samples $\overline{\text{BUSRQ}}$ at the leading edge of ϕ during the last clock period of every machine cycle. If $\overline{\text{BUSRQ}}$ is sampled low, the Z-80 floats the address and data buses and lowers $\overline{\text{BUSAK}}$. The lowering of $\overline{\text{BUSAK}}$ signals external logic that the buses have been floated. The Z-80 continues sampling $\overline{\text{BUSRQ}}$ at the leading edge of every subsequent ϕ pulse. As soon as $\overline{\text{BUSRQ}}$ is found to be high, the buses are connected to the Z-80 at the leading edge of the next ϕ pulse.

When a Z-80 enters the hold state, it ceases to refresh the dynamic

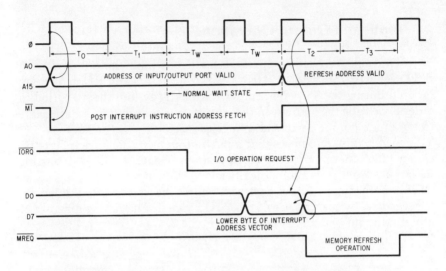

Fig. 4.8 Postinterrupt fetch phase, in which lower byte of interrupt address vector is fetched from the device (Mode 2)

RAMs. The external logic either must perform this operation or not force the Z-80 into a hold state for long periods of time.

A Z-80 enters a halt state by lowering $\overline{\text{HALT}}$ after executing a halt instruction. In the halt state, a Z-80 simply does not stop all operations and wait for an external interrupt. If this were the case, the memory refreshing operation would have ceased. To keep the memory refreshing operation going, a Z-80 executes a sequence of no operation instructions (NOPs) while waiting for an external interrupt. Thus, the halt state of a Z-80 is not the same as that of an 8080A. In fact, a Z-80 has no halt state in the strictest sense of the word.

Interrupt Handling

The highest priority interrupt for a Z-80 is the nonmaskable interrupt that uses the $\overline{\text{NMI}}$ input signal. A Z-80 samples $\overline{\text{NMI}}$ at the leading edge of ϕ during the last clock period of a machine cycle. If $\overline{\text{NMI}}$ is low, then during the next machine cycle, the Z-80 executes a restart RSTn type of instruction and branches to memory location 102. From that point on, it executes an interrupt service routine to prepare the system for an impending power failure.

All other interrupt requests to a Z-80 lower the $\overline{\text{INT}}$ input signal, which is also sampled at the leading edge of ϕ during the last clock period of a machine cycle. Note that $\overline{\text{BUSRQ}}$ is also sampled at the same time. If both $\overline{\text{INT}}$ and $\overline{\text{BUSRQ}}$ are found to be low, then the request for floating the system bus is honored first.

At the start of the next machine cycle following a low value of $\overline{INT}$, a Z-80 enters an interrupt acknowledge phase. During this phase, a branch instruction or the lower byte of an address is fetched from the interrupting device. Since this is an instruction fetch operation, the Z-80 lowers $\overline{MI}$. However, since this instruction is fetched from an input/output device, the Z-80 sets $\overline{IORQ}$ to a low value. A wait state lasting two clock periods is automatically added to the machine cycle to give external logic enough time to resolve priority of multiple interrupts. The timing diagram is shown in Fig. 4.8.

A Z-80 can operate in three different interrupt modes. In mode 0, the interrupting device responds with the object code of a restart (RST n) instruction—a procedure identical to the interrupt handling of an 8080A. In mode 1, the Z-80 assumes that the object code is a restart instruction and branches to memory location 86. This is an efficient method for handling single interrupts that come from only one device. The alternative set of registers can be used to eliminate the process of saving and restoring of register contents in memory.

In interrupt mode 2, a Z-80 treats the byte supplied by the interrupting device as the lower byte of an address in memory. The upper byte of the address is obtained from the contents of the interrupt vector register in the Z-80. The Z-80 then saves all the register contents in a stack in memory (using the stack pointer SP for addressing), fetches the contents of the previously mentioned memory location as the next instruction, and starts servicing the interrupt. This mode of interrupt handling is shown in Fig. 4.9.

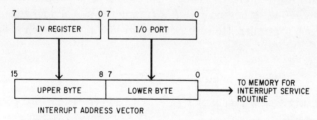

Fig. 4.9 Vectored interrupt address handling (Mode 2)

8080A/Z-80 Replacement Considerations

Recall that the instruction set of an 8080A is a subset of the instruction set of a Z-80. Thus, programs written for an 8080A will execute on a Z-80, but the converse is not true. Therefore, it is not possible to replace a Z-80 by an 8080A unless the existing software is also replaced. However, an 8080A can be replaced by a Z-80 without affecting the existing software, provided the job is done with some care.

An 8080A and a Z-80, as mentioned earlier, are not pin compatible. Nor does a Z-80 provide all the signals provided by an 8080A and its associated 8228 bus controller. Since a single Z-80 microprocessor chip can replace three 8080 system chips (8080A, 8224, and 8228), problems of signal compatibility can seriously affect the 8080 support chips.

The 8080 support chips depend on four read/write signals generated by the 8228 controller; these are $\overline{\text{MEMR}}$, $\overline{\text{MEMW}}$, $\overline{\text{IOR}}$, and $\overline{\text{IQW}}$. A Z-80 chip generates four different signals; these are $\overline{\text{MREQ}}$, $\overline{\text{IORQ}}$, $\overline{\text{RD}}$ and $\overline{\text{WR}}$. Figure 4.10 shows one possible way of obtaining the read/write signals needed by the 8080 support chips from the Z-80 microprocessor signals.

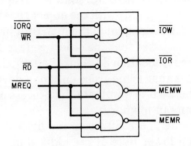

Fig. 4.10   8080A read/write signals from corresponding signals of a Z-80

In an 8080 system, the input/output devices are selected by decoding the contents of the address bus alone. In a Z-80 system, the memory units and the input/output devices are differentiated by means of the $\overline{\text{MREQ}}$ and $\overline{\text{IORQ}}$ signals. Therefore, these signals must be carefully incorporated into the select/decode logic of the 8080 support systems.

The Z-80 chip has no $\overline{\text{INTA}}$ signal, such as the one generated by the 8228 bus controller. However, as shown in Fig. 4.11, such a signal can

Fig. 4.11   Generation of INTA for 8080 support chips from Z-80 signals

be created by combining $\overline{\text{MI}}$ and $\overline{\text{IORQ}}$ of the Z-80. The HOLD and HLDA signals of an 8080A are functionally equivalent to the $\overline{\text{BUSRQ}}$ and $\overline{\text{BUSAK}}$ signals of a Z-80. There is no signal in Z-80 that identifies the first clock period of every machine cycle like the SYNC signal of an 8080A. It may be possible to use an inverted MI, but this signal will remain high for the first two time periods.

Signals such as INTE, WAIT, and ϕ_2 (TTL) of an 8080 system have no counterparts in a Z-80 based system. Any 8080 system component that uses ϕ_2 (TTL) simply cannot be used with a Z-80 system. Lack of an INTE should not be a serious handicap. INTE informs the peripheral devices when the microprocessor has disabled all interrupts.

Such information is not really critical since even if a device requests an interrupt in the absence of INTE, the microprocessor can always ignore it. However, if the operation of a device depends on INTE, then its interface may have to be reconfigured. There is no simple way to create a WAIT signal out of the signals from a Z-80 that will be equivalent to the WAIT signal of an 8080A. Since a Z-80 sometimes inserts automatic wait states, it is necessary to decode various object codes, timing signals, and so on, to create a WAIT signal. Recall also that a Z-80 does not have a true halt state. In the halt state, it executes a sequence of NOPs to maintain the memory refreshing operation going.

Z-80 Programmable Parallel Input/Output Port

The parallel input/output port (PIO) of a Z-80 system is much more versatile than the simple 8212 port discussed in Chap. 3. It can be programmed to carry out parallel data transfer under different conditions. However, it is also much more complex and difficult to use than the 8212 port. The Z-80 PIO has 16 input/output lines grouped into two eight-bit parallel input/output ports, port A and port B, respectively. Under program control, each port can be designated either as an input port, an output port, or a control port. Each line of a control port can be individually assigned for input or output. Port A can also be used as a bidirectional input/output port. Furthermore, a Z-80 PIO offers considerable facilities for interrupt handling. Figure 4.12 shows the pin assignments and signal descriptions of a Z-80 PIO, whereas Fig. 4.13 provides a functional description of the port.

PIO Select Logic and Functions

There are three select lines on the Z-80 PIO—$\overline{CE}$, B/$\overline{A}$, and C/$\overline{D}$. The $\overline{CE}$, the master chip enable signal, must be set low to select the PIO chip. The B/$\overline{A}$ selects port B if high and port A if low. The C/$\overline{D}$ signal, if high, selects the control buffer and, if low, the data buffer. The codes for the selection of all the buffers in a PIO are shown in Table 4.1.

Table 4.1 Buffer Selection Codes

$\overline{CE}$	B/$\overline{A}$	C/$\overline{D}$	Selected buffer
0	0	0	Data buffer of Port A
0	1	0	Data buffer of Port B
0	0	1	Control buffer of Port A
0	1	1	Control buffer of Port B
1	X	X	PIO not selected

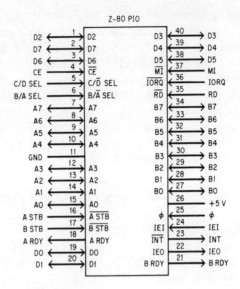

Pin Name	Description	Type
DO–D7	Data Bus	Tristate, bidirectional
$\overline{CE}$	Device Enable	Input
B/$\overline{A}$ SEL	Select Port A or Port B	Input
C/$\overline{D}$ SEL	Select Control or Data	Input
$\overline{MI}$	Instruction fetch machine cycle signal from CPU	Input
$\overline{IORQ}$	Input/Output Request from CPU	Input
$\overline{RD}$	Read cycle status from CPU	Input
A0–A7	Port A Bus	Tristate, bidirectional
A RDY	Register A Ready	Output
$\overline{A}$ $\overline{STB}$	Port A Strobe pulse	Input
B0–B7	Port B Bus	Tristate, bidirectional
B RDY	Register B Ready	Output
$\overline{B}$ $\overline{STB}$	Port B Strobe pulse	Input
IEI	Interrupt Enable In	Input
IEO	Interrupt Enable Out	Output
$\overline{INT}$	Interrupt Request	Output
ϕ, +5V, GND	Clock, Power, and Ground	

Fig. 4.12   Z-80 PIO chip

The output signals $\overline{MI}$, $\overline{IORQ}$, and $\overline{RD}$ of a Z-80 microprocessor are used as input signals to the Z-80 PIO. The direction of data transfer is specified by means of these signals. Since the PIO has some interrupt handling capabilities, they also specify an interrupt acknowledge condition and a check for the end of an interrupt service routine. The codes used for these conditions are shown in Table 4.2.

$\overline{IORQ}$ = 0 and $\overline{RD}$ = 0 denote a standard read from an input device, and similarly $\overline{MI}$ = 0 and $\overline{IORQ}$ = 0 denote a standard signal for the start of an interrupt acknowledgement cycle. However, $\overline{WR}$ is not

Table 4.2 $\overline{MI}$, $\overline{IORQ}$, and $\overline{RD}$ Codes

$\overline{MI}$	$\overline{IORQ}$	$\overline{RD}$	Interpretation
1	0	0	Transfer from PIO to microprocessor (read)
1	0	1	Transfer from microprocessor to PIO (write)
0	0	1	Interrupt acknowledge
0	1	0	Check for end of service routine
0	1	1	Reset PIO

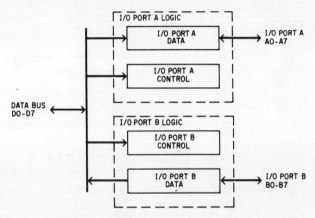

Fig. 4.13 Fundamental description of a Z-80 PIO

used to trigger a write into an output device; rather, $\overline{RD}$ = 1 is used along with $\overline{IORQ}$ = 0. This is not the convention used by a Z-80 microprocessor at its interface.

PIO Operating Modes and Protocols

A Z-80 PIO can operate in five different modes using two different protocols. It can operate in the output or input mode with the handshaking protocol (modes 0 and 1), bidirectional input/output mode with the handshaking protocol (mode 2), control mode (mode 3), and simple input or output mode (mode 4). The handshaking protocol is implemented by using signals RDY, $\overline{STB}$, and $\overline{INT}$. The most important modes—0, 1, and 2—are discussed in detail below:

Mode 0:   Either port A or port B can be used as an output port with handshaking to transfer data from a Z-80 microprocessor to peripheral devices. An output operation starts whenever the microprocessor selects a suitable port of the PIO and executes an output instruction. The

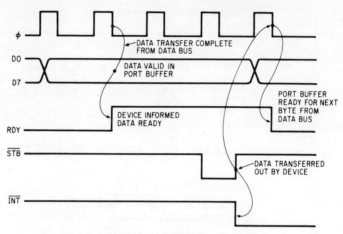

Fig. 4.14 Data output operation via PIO (Mode 0)

PIO decodes the input signals, as explained in the previous section, to determine the port selected and the type of data transfer requested (output).

After the microprocessor transfers data from the data bus into the selected ports data buffer, the PIO sets the corresponding RDY signal high. This signal informs the peripheral device controller that data are available in the data buffer of the port. The device controller acknowledges completion of a data transfer by pulsing $\overline{STB}$ low. The following trailing edge of the clock pulse ϕ resets RDY and the trailing edge of the $\overline{STB}$ low pulse generates an interrupt request from the PIO ($\overline{INT}$ low). The timing diagram is shown in Fig. 4.14.

Mode 1:   In the input mode, the device controller sets $\overline{STB}$ low when data is ready for transfer. In response to this, the PIO transfers data from the input/output lines into the port's data buffer. The trailing edge of the $\overline{STB}$ pulse also triggers an interrupt request from the PIO ($\overline{INT}$ low). The trailing edge of the next clock pulse ϕ lowers RDY to inform the device controller that data is in the PIO buffer. When the microprocessor transfers this data out of the buffer, it resets RDY to high. As long as RDY is low, the device controller should refrain from transferring any new data into the PIO buffer. The timing diagram for this operation is shown in Fig. 4.15.

Mode 2:   In the bidirectional input/output mode, port A is used for the data transfer. The control signals of port B are used in conjunction with the control signals of port A to implement the handshaking protocol for bidirectional transfer. Hence, port B must operate in the control mode (mode 3). The timing diagram is shown in Fig. 4.16. The ARDY and $\overline{ASTB}$ signals are used to control the data output operation. The data input operation is controlled by the BSTB and $\overline{BRDY}$ signals.

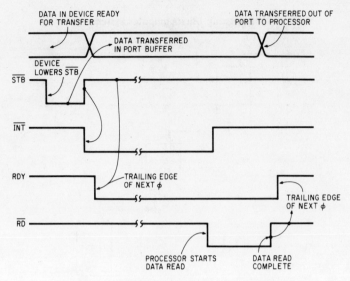

Fig. 4.15   Data input operation via PIO (Mode 1)

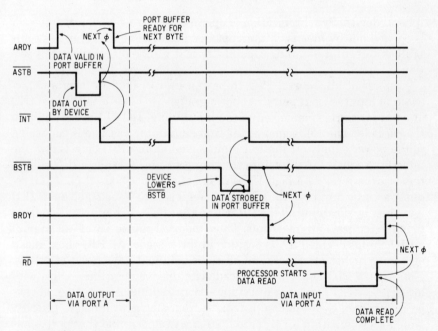

Fig. 4.16   Bidirectional data transfer (port A transfers data; port B provides control)

PIO Interrupt Handling

As discussed in the previous section, the $\overline{STB}$ and RDY signals are used to implement handshaking protocol between a PIO port and a per-

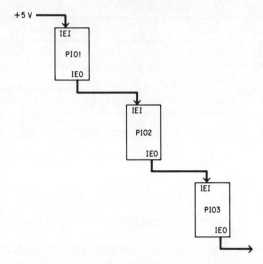

Fig. 4.17 Cascading several PIOs in a daisy chain

ipheral device. Synchronization of operations with a Z-80 microprocessor is carried out by means of interrupt signal $\overline{\text{INT}}$. The PIO chip has some built-in interrupt handling capabilities that will be discussed in this section.

First of all, several PIO chips can be cascaded to form a *daisy-chain* of input/output ports, as shown in Fig. 4.17. The output signal IEO of one PIO chip is connected to the input signal IEI of the next chip in the cascade. The IEI signal of the first chip in the cascade is connected to the power supply. If the IEI input signal of any PIO chip is low, the interrupt request circuit within the chip is disabled. When a PIO chip in the cascade receives a high IEI signal from the previous chip, it can request an interrupt by setting $\overline{\text{INT}}$ low. As it sets $\overline{\text{INT}}$ low, it also sets IEO low, thereby disabling all the PIO chips after it since they are now unable to make requests for interrupts. Thus, the level of priority of interrupt of a PIO chip is decided by its position in the cascade. All PIO chips ahead of it have higher priorities, and all chips behind it have lower priorities. Note that a PIO chip in the cascade can disable only those chips with lower priorities. Thus, the interrupt service routine of a chip can always be interrupted by an interrupt request from a chip with higher priority. Note also that within a PIO chip there are two ports and that port A has higher priority than port B.

Since a PIO chip within a cascade can disable the interrupt systems of all chips with lower priorities, it is also responsible for re-enabling them. A PIO chip looks for the last instruction of its interrupt service routine, and when it detects that, it re-enables all lower priority chips. The last instruction of an interrupt service routine is a RETI instruction (return from interrupt routine). Whenever $\overline{\text{MI}}$ is low, a PIO whose interrupt has been acknowledged samples the object code of the instruction on the data bus. When this object code matches the RETI object code, it re-enables all lower priority PIO chips.

A port in a PIO can be programmed to operate in the control mode (mode 3). In this mode, the user can designate individual port lines to be either input lines or output lines. A port in the control mode can be used to monitor external events and interrupt the Z-80 microprocessor when a predefined set of values (zeros and ones) appear on the designated input lines.

PIO Programming

A PIO port can operate in different modes. The mode of operation of a port is determined by a control word that is transferred to the selected port's control buffer. The format of the mode specification control word is shown below:

7	6	5	4	3	2	1	0
		X	X	1	1	1	1

Bits B0, . . . , B3 of such a control word are always 1s. The choice of values for B4 and B5 are immaterial for mode specification. The values of B6 and B7 are selected as shown in Table 4.3.

Table 4.3 Mode Specification

B7	B6	Mode Specification
0	0	Mode 0 (output mode)
0	1	Mode 1 (input mode)
1	0	Mode 2 (bidirectional transfer)
1	1	Mode 3 (control mode)

The following control word is used to specify whether the interrupt request from a port is to be enabled or disabled:

7	6	5	4	3	2	1	0
	X	X	X	0	0	1	1

B7 = 0 disables interrupt requests and B7 = 1 enables them. If a Z-80 microprocessor is operating in interrupt mode 2, then when a PIO port interrupts it, the microprocessor will expect the port to supply the lower byte of an interrupt address. This address byte is stored in the port by using the following control word:

7	6	5	4	3	2	1	0
							0

B0 = 0 instructs the selected port that this control word specifies the lower byte of the interrupt address vector; it is to be used by the port when requesting an interrupt. B1, . . . , B7 are used to specify the actual address to be used by the port.

Z-80 Clock Timer Circuit

The functions of a Z-80 clock timer circuit (CTC) are similar to those of the 8253 programmable counter/timer discussed in Chap. 3. The Z-80 CTC has four independently programmable timer circuits as opposed to three such circuits for the 8253. However, the 8253 has more programmable options than the Z-80 CTC. Each timer circuit inside a CTC is called a *channel*. Figure 4.18 shows the pin assignments and the signal descriptions of a Z-80 CTC. The functional diagram of a CTC channel is shown in Fig. 4.19.

Each channel of a CTC has three eight-bit registers, called the *control register,* the *time constant register,* and the *down-count register.* The starting value of a channel timer is stored in the time constant register. At the start of a countdown, this value is transferred into the down-count register. In the timer mode of operation, a channel uses master clock pulse ϕ from a Z-80 microprocessor to decrement the contents of the down-count register. The process of decrementation is carried out either at every sixteenth clock pulse or at every two-hundred-and-fifty-sixth clock pulse. If the period of the master clock is 500 ns, then register contents are decremented at every 8- or 128-μs interval. Each channel has a separate CLK/TRG input line for triggering the timing logic. The master clock signal ϕ is used for a timer; signals from external logic can be used if the channel serves as an event counter.

CTC Select Logic and Functions

The $\overline{CE}$ is the master chip enable signal; it must be low for the CTC chip to be selected. The four separate channels are selected by means of the CS0 and CS1 input signals as shown in Table 4.4.

The specific register selected within a channel is decided by the following control word on the data bus:

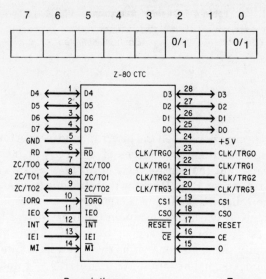

Pin Name	Description	Type
D0–D7	Data Bus	Tristate, bidirectional
CLK/TRG0 CLK/TRG1 CLK/TRG2 CLK/TRG3	External Clock or Timer Trigger	
ZC/TO0 ZC/TO1 ZC/TO2	Zero Count or Timeout Indicator	Output
MI	Instruction fetch machine cycle signal from CPU	Input
IORQ	Input/Output Request from CPU	Input
RD	Read cycle status from CPU	Input
RESET	Device Reset	Input
IEI	Interrupt Enable In	Input
IEO	Interrupt Enable Out	Output
INT	Interrupt Request	Output
CE	Device Enable	Input
CS0, CS1	Register Select	Input
ϕ, + 5V, GND	Clock, Power, and Ground	

Fig. 4.18 Control timer chip

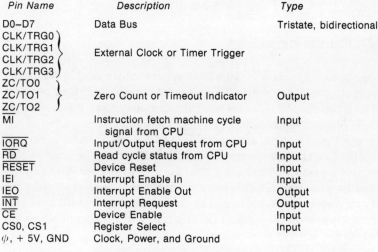

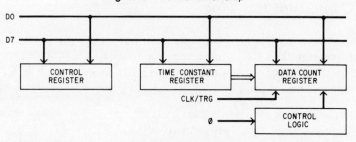

Fig. 4.19 Functional description of a channel of CTC

Table 4.4 Channel Selection

CS1	CS0	Channel selected
0	0	0
0	1	1
1	0	2
1	1	3

B0 = 0 selects channel 0 when the interrupt address vector is specified. The interrupt handling capabilities of a CTC will be discussed later. B0 = 1 means that the control register of the selected channel is used during the first access. B2 = 0 means that the time constant register is accessed by the following write instruction. B2 = 1 means that the channel control register is selected again on the next write. $\overline{MI}$, $\overline{IORQ}$, and $\overline{RD}$ are the three other input signals to a CTC. Their values are interpreted in exactly the same manner as those of a PIO. Since a CTC has a separate $\overline{RESET}$ signal as input, $\overline{MI}$ = 0, $\overline{IORQ}$ = 1 and $\overline{RD}$ = 1 are no longer interpreted as a reset condition.

CTC Operating Modes

The operating modes of each channel are rather simple compared to the operating modes of an 8253. Each channel operates either as a timer or as a counter. In either case, at the end of a count, the corresponding ZC/TO output signal is set to a high value for one clock period. If the interrupt logic has been enabled, then an $\overline{INT}$ low signal is generated at this point. The channel then resets itself and starts the countdown all over again. If a new value has been inserted in the time constant register in the middle of a countdown, then this new value is used to reset the channel at the end of a countdown. The countdown can be initiated by an external logic pulse on the CLK/TRG input line when a channel is operating as a timer.

CTC Interrupt Handling

Each Z-80 CTC chip has an input IEI and an output IEO signal along with the standard $\overline{INT}$ interrupt request signal. Thus, a CTC can be cascaded into a daisy chain along with the PIOs, as shown in Fig. 4.17. The order of priority of interrupt requests among the channels is as follows:

Channel 0   Highest priority
Channel 1   Next lower priority
Channel 2   Next lower priority
Channel 3   Lowest priority

A CTC makes an interrupt request by lowering the $\overline{\text{INT}}$ signal. A Z-80 microprocessor acknowledges this request in the standard manner with $\overline{\text{MI}} = 0$ and $\overline{\text{IORQ}} = 0$. If the microprocessor is operating in interrupt mode 2, then the CTC transmits the lower byte of an interrupt address vector over the data bus. It also lowers the IEO signal, thereby disabling all devices with lower priority in the cascaded daisy chain.

CTC Programming

A channel in a CTC can operate in different modes. The operation of a channel is controlled by means of control words transmitted via the data bus. The format of a control word is shown below:

7	6	5	4	3	2	1	0
							1

B0 of all control words is always one. B1 = 1 is used to stop the channel from counting down. When B1 = 1, the countdown stops immediately, the output signal ZC/TO remains inactive, and the interrupt circuitry is disabled. If B2 = 1, then the next data sent over the data bus is interpreted as a new value for the time constant register. If B2 = 0, then the next data is interpreted either as another control code (B0 = 1) or an interrupt vector (B0 = 0). If the channel is operating as a timer, then B3 = 0 means that the countdown signals are derived from the master clock pulse ϕ. If B3 = 1, then a pulse on the CLK/TRG input line triggers the timer.

If B7 = 0, then the interrupt circuitry of the channel is disabled; if B7 = 1, then it is enabled. B6 selects the timer/counter mode. B6 = 0 implies a timer and B6 = 1 implies a counter. If B6 = 1 and B3 = 0, then every pulse on the CLK/TRG line decrements the counter (event counter mode).

B4 determines whether the leading edge or the trailing edge of the pulse on the CLK/TRG line is used for a countdown. B4 = 1 selects the leading edge and B4 = 0 selects the trailing edge. In the timer mode of operation, if B5 = 0, then countdown takes place at every sixteenth clock pulse. Otherwise, it occurs at every two-hundred-and-fifty-sixth clock pulse.

The lower byte of an interrupt vector to be used by a CTC is specified by an interrupt control word of the following form:

7	6	5	4	3	2	1	0
					X	X	C

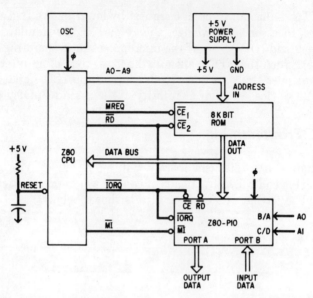

Fig. 4.20   Minimum configuration of a Z-80 microcomputer system

For an interrupt control word, B0 is always zero. B1 and B2 are ignored, and the interrupt address byte of a CTC is always specified for channel 0. B3, . . . , B7 specifies the interrupt address for the CTC.

To program a CTC, an interrupt address is first specified during an initialization procedure. One or more control words are then used for each channel to set the mode of operation (counter/timer), initialize the time constant register, and so forth. Subsequent control words are used to start or stop the channels or to reinitialize the counters.

A functional diagram of a minimum Z-80 microcomputer configuration is shown in Fig. 4.20.

Chapter 5

Motorola MC6800 System

Introduction

The Motorola MC6800 microprocessor system, manufactured by Motorola Inc., was designed as an enhancement of Intel's original 8008 microprocessor. Hence, it should be classified with and compared to Intel's 8080 system rather than the more recent Z-80. The MC6800 uses a single +5 V power supply and a very simple timing and control sequence. Each machine cycle in an MC6800 lasts for exactly one clock period, as opposed to the variable number of clock periods for an 8080A. The MC6800 generates and uses a very simple set of control signals. For this reason, no 8228-type special bus controllers are necessary, and the need for data bus multiplexing between data and status information is eliminated. The MC6800 also uses the memory-mapped input/output technique in which programmable registers in peripheral interfaces are addressed as memory locations. The instruction set of an MC6800 is designed in a more systematic manner. Fewer basic types of instructions with various modes of memory addressing are necessary for a system that uses memory-mapped input/output operations.

Being one of the earlier microprocessors along with the 8080A, the MC6800 also needs a separate clock generator circuit. It also suffers from a dearth of addressable registers in the microprocessor and a register to register instructions. Availability of only two accumulators forces programmers to make excessive use of memory reference instructions. All support chips of the MC6800 require a special synchronizing signal, to be discussed later. As a result, these support chips cannot be used with other microprocessors. It is reasonable to assume that future enhancements of the MC6800 microprocessor will eliminate some or all of these undesirable features.

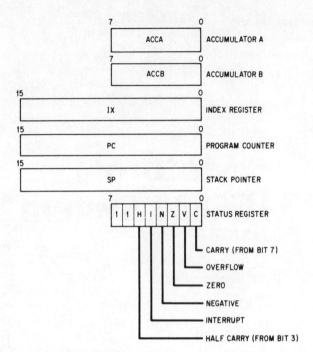

Fig. 5.1   Addressable registers of an MC6800

MC6800 Microprocessor

The addressable registers of a MC6800 microprocessor are shown in Fig. 5.1. There are two eight-bit primary accumulators, one eight-bit status register, three 16-bit registers, an index register, program counter, and stack pointer, respectively. All instructions referencing an accumulator can address any one of them. The contents of the status register, however, can be transferred only to accumulator A. Since the MC6800 does not have an explicit data counter, the stack pointer is often used to address operands. By saving and restoring the contents of the index register and the stack pointer in RAM, these registers can be put to multiple use.

The MC6800 microprocessor chip with its pin assignments and signal descriptions is shown in Fig. 5.2. The address bus is a tristate bus with 16 lines, A0, ..., A15, and is used to address memory as well as peripheral interfaces. The data bus is a standard tristate bus with eight lines, D0, ..., D7. The read/write signal $(R/\overline{W})$ is used to select the direction of data transfer on the data bus. Normally, it has a high value, which indicates a data read operation when the microprocessor uses the data bus. Otherwise, a low value indicates a data write operation. VMA (Valid Memory Address) is a special signal for the MC6800 that is set high whenever the microprocessor puts a valid address on the address bus. $\overline{IRQ}$ is the standard interrupt signal ($\overline{INT}$) for the MC6800. If the interrupt requests have been enabled by the microprocessor and the latter is *not* in the halt state, it accepts interrupt requests via $\overline{IRQ}$. Note the difference in operation here; when in the halt state, an 8080A and a Z-80 wait for an external interrupt. The nonmaskable interrupt line $\overline{NMI}$ and the reset line $\overline{RESET}$ are functionally identical with equivalent signals for a Z-80.

The MC6800 uses four signals—TSC, DBE, $\overline{HALT}$, and BA—to

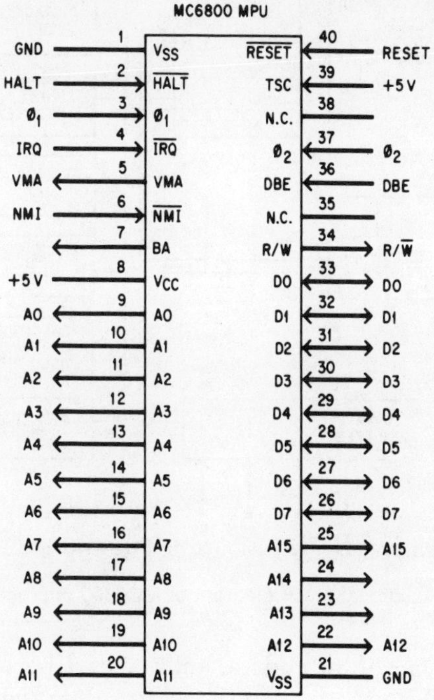

MC6800 MPU

Pin	Left Signal	Pin# L	Right Signal	Pin# R	External
GND	V_{SS}	1	$\overline{RESET}$	40	RESET
HALT	$\overline{HALT}$	2	TSC	39	+5 V
ϕ_1	ϕ_1	3	N.C.	38	
IRQ	$\overline{IRQ}$	4	ϕ_2	37	ϕ_2
VMA	VMA	5	DBE	36	DBE
NMI	$\overline{NMI}$	6	N.C.	35	
	BA	7	R/W	34	R/$\overline{W}$
+5 V	V_{CC}	8	D0	33	D0
A0	A0	9	D1	32	D1
A1	A1	10	D2	31	D2
A2	A2	11	D3	30	D3
A3	A3	12	D4	29	D4
A4	A4	13	D5	28	D5
A5	A5	14	D6	27	D6
A6	A6	15	D7	26	D7
A7	A7	16	A15	25	A15
A8	A8	17	A14	24	
A9	A9	18	A13	23	
A10	A10	19	A12	22	A12
A11	A11	20	V_{SS}	21	GND

Pin Name	Description	Type
A0–A15	Address lines	Tristate, output
D0–D7	Data Bus lines	Tristate, bidirectional
$\overline{HALT}$	Halt	Input
TSC	Three State Control	Input
R/$\overline{W}$	Read/Write	Tristate, Output
VMA	Valid Memory Address	Output
DBE	Data Bus Enable	Input
BA	Bus Available	Output
$\overline{IRQ}$	Interrupt Request	Input
$\overline{RESET}$	Reset	Input
$\overline{NMI}$	NonMaskable Interrupt	Input
ϕ_1, ϕ_2	Clock signals	Input
V_{SS}, V_{CC}	Power	

Fig. 5.2 (a) MC6800 microprocessor chip

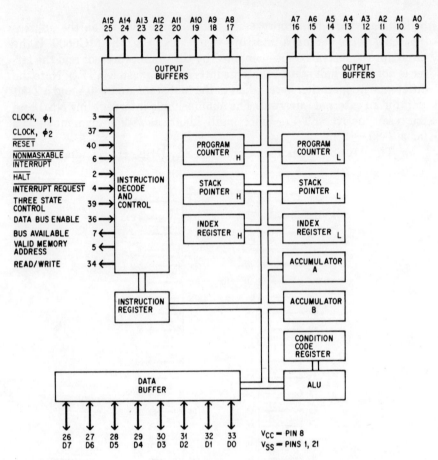

Fig. 5.2 (b) Functional block diagram of MC6800 microprocessor chip

control the operations of the address and the data buses. The three-state control signal TSC is used to float the address bus and the output of the R/$\overline{\text{W}}$ signal. The data bus enable signal DBE is input low to float the data bus. When the $\overline{\text{HALT}}$ signal is lowered, the microprocessor stops instruction execution and floats the entire system bus. When the system bus is floated following a $\overline{\text{HALT}}$ low input, the bus available signal BA is raised. A low value on BA indicates that the system bus is being used by the microprocessor.

MC6800 Timing and Instruction Execution

The MC6800 microprocessor, as does the 8080A, uses a two-phase clock (ϕ_1, ϕ_2). However, clock signals for an MC6800 are arranged differently from those of an 8080A. These signals are shown in Fig. 5.3. Note

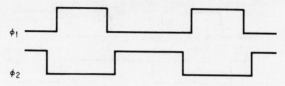

Fig. 5.3 MC6800 clock signals ϕ_1 and ϕ_2

that the high pulse of one clock signal always occurs during the low pulse of the other. Each machine cycle of the MC6800 lasts for only one clock period; the relationship of a machine cycle to a clock period is shown in Fig. 5.4.

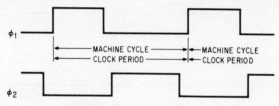

Fig. 5.4 Relationship between a clock period and a machine cycle

Memory Read and Write

The basic data transfer operations of an MC6800 microprocessor consist of a memory read and a memory write. An instruction fetch is not distinguished from an operand fetch by means of any special output signal. The basic memory read and write operations take one machine cycle, that is, one clock period.

The timing diagram of a memory read operation is shown in Fig. 5.5. The leading edge of the ϕ_1 pulse transfers the contents of the program counter onto the address bus and raises VMA to denote a valid memory address output from the microprocessor. The $R/\overline{W}$ signal is raised to indicate a memory read operation. The contents of the addressed memory word is placed on the data bus during the later part of the machine cycle. The trailing edge of the ϕ_2 pulse transfers the data in from the data bus and resets $R/\overline{W}$ and VMA.

The timing diagram of a memory write operation is shown in Fig. 5.6. The address output and the setting of the VMA signal are done as they are for the read operation. The $R/\overline{W}$ signal is set low to indicate a write operation. However, valid data does not appear on the data bus at the start of the write machine cycle. The trailing edge of the ϕ_2 pulse (Fig. 5.6) lowers the DBE signal temporarily, thereby floating the data bus. In most MC6800 systems, DBE and ϕ_2 are identical, in which case DBE stays low as long as ϕ_2 remains low. Shortly after the rise of DBE, the

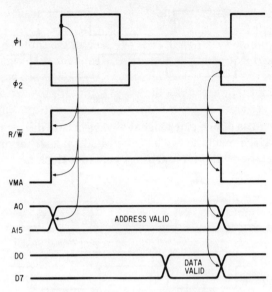

Fig. 5.5   Memory read operation

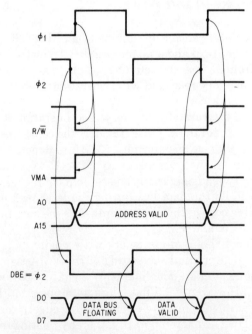

Fig. 5.6   Memory write operation with DBE = ϕ_2

data that is to be written is transferred to the data bus from the micro-processor.

Slow memory operations are accommodated by means of stretching the duration of clock signals. Means for such signal stretching are built into the clock signal generator. Whenever the microprocessor carries out internal operations that do not require the use of the system bus, VMA is set low and R/W is set high. Note that the VMA and DBE signals are used to mark those machine cycles when the microprocessor is using the system bus.

Wait State

The wait state of an MC6800 has a different significance than the wait states of an 8080A and a Z-80. Wait states are used by the latter to accommodate slow memory operations when the microprocessor waits for data. An MC6800 uses a wait state to wait for an interrupt request. The microprocessor enters a wait state by executing a WAI instruction when it has nothing to do except wait for an interrupt. The execution of a WAI instruction automatically stores all register contents in a stack in the memory, using the stack pointer for the purpose of addressing. At the completion of the execution of a WAI instruction, the microprocessor floats the system bus, raises the bus available signal BA, and waits for an interrupt. A timing diagram of the execution of the WAI instruction is shown in Fig. 5.7.

Since the system bus is floated in the wait state, it can be used to transfer blocks of data between a peripheral device and memory without interfering with the operations of the microprocessor. Completion of such a transfer is signaled by an interrupt request that puts the micro-processor back into operation.

Hold and Halt States

The MC6800 does not have an explicit hold state like an 8080A or a Z-80. However, a hold state can be induced by means of the TSC signal. For simplicity, it is assumed that the DBE and ϕ_2 signals are identical. If the TSC signal is lowered, it floats the address bus and the $R/\overline{W}$ and VMA signals. Thus, if the TSC signal is lowered while ϕ_1 is high and ϕ_2 (DBE) is low and if the clock signals are held constant by stretching, the entire system bus floats. A timing diagram for this sequence of operations is shown in Fig. 5.8. This state cannot last for too long since the MC6800 needs to refresh the contents of its internal registers. However, this state is similar to the usual hold state of an 8080A or a Z-80.

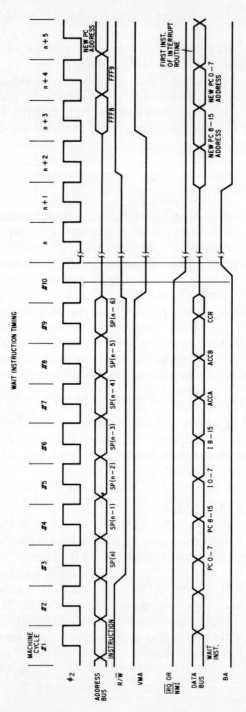

Fig. 5.7 Execution of the WAIT instruction

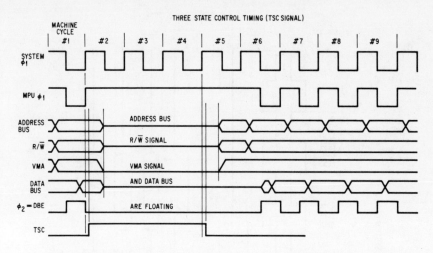

Fig. 5.8 Floating system bus and signals by raising TSC (DBE = ϕ_2)

The halt state of the MC6800 is not the same as the halt state of an 8080A. An MC6800 does not enter its halt state by executing a halt instruction. Whenever the input signal $\overline{\text{HALT}}$ is low, the MC6800 enters a halt state upon completion of the execution of the current instruction. In the halt state, the microprocessor floats the system bus and the R/$\overline{\text{W}}$ signal, lowers the VMA signal, and raises the bus available signal BA (see Fig. 5.9). As long as $\overline{\text{HALT}}$ is low, it remains in the halt state.

Interrupt Handling

The interrupt handling scheme used by a MC6800 is diametrically opposite to that used by a Z-80. In a Z-80 system, the interrupting device provides the lower byte of an interrupt address vector that is used by the microprocessor to fetch the first instruction of an appropriate service routine. This is known as the *vectored interrupt system.* In an MC6800 system, all interrupts from peripheral devices cause the microprocessor to branch to a single location in memory. This location specifies the start of a general-purpose service routine that polls the devices to find the source of the interrupt and, in case of multiple interrupts, arbitrates priorities of service.

The MC6800 microprocessor does distinguish among certain categories of interrupt requests and assigns a fixed order of priorities to them. The categories are as follows:

Restart   Highest priority

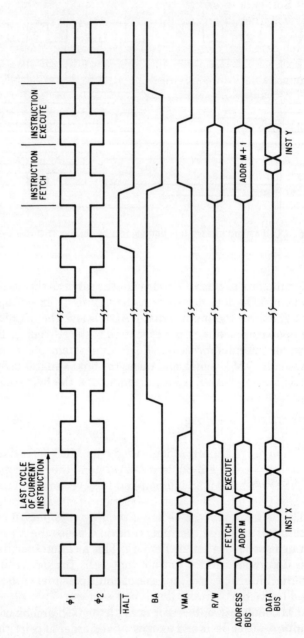

Fig. 5.9   Effects of lowering the HALT signal

Nonmaskable interrupt   Next lower priority
Software interrupt   Next lower priority
External interrupt   Lowest priority

In each case, the microprocessor branches to a different location in memory. External device interrupts are made by lowering input line $\overline{\text{IRQ}}$. Nonmaskable interrupts are indicated by lowering $\overline{\text{NMI}}$. A nonmaskable interrupt is one such as a power failure, and its service routine terminates the microprocessor operations in a graceful manner. A restart, on the other hand, is caused by turning power on, and its service routine initiates operations of the microprocessor.

A software interrupt is caused during a normal instruction execution by such conditions as illegal instruction code, division by zero, and the like, that make it impossible to execute the instruction. When such a condition is detected, the microprocessor executes a software interrupt SWI instruction. This instruction causes the microprocessor to go through the same sequence of operations as an external interrupt would and starts execution of a service routine to handle the error condition.

An MC6800 acknowledges an interrupt request at the end of the execution of the current instruction (maybe a SWI) and disables the interrupt system. It then automatically stores the contents of the internal registers in a stack in memory in the following order: (1) lower byte of PC, (2) upper byte of PC, (3) lower byte of index register, (4) upper byte of index register, (5) accumulator A, (6) accumulator B, and (7) status register. This sequence of events is shown in Fig. 5.10. In an 8080A system, explicit machine language instructions are needed to store all register contents following an interrupt. After storing the register contents, an MC6800 uses the next two machine cycles to fetch the contents of the memory location assigned to the interrupt of a given category (that is, software interrupt, external interrupt, and the like).

MC6800/8080 Signal Conversion

Intel's 8080 support chips are very often used with an MC6800 microprocessor. The signal conversions necessary to accomplish this are rather straightforward (Fig. 5.11). The $R/\overline{W}$ output signal from a MC6800 is decomposed into two separate signals, $\overline{\text{RD}}$ and $\overline{\text{WR}}$, for the 8080 support chips. The HOLD signal from a support chip is inverted and applied to the $\overline{\text{HALT}}$ input line. The $\overline{\text{INT}}$ signal from a support chip or a PICU is connected to the $\overline{\text{IRQ}}$ input line. The INTA signal for the support chips must be obtained by combining the VMA with the decoded contents of the address bus that addresses the memory location used by the MC6800 for handling external interrupts. Since the MC6800 uses memory-mapped input/output, such decoding of the contents of the ad-

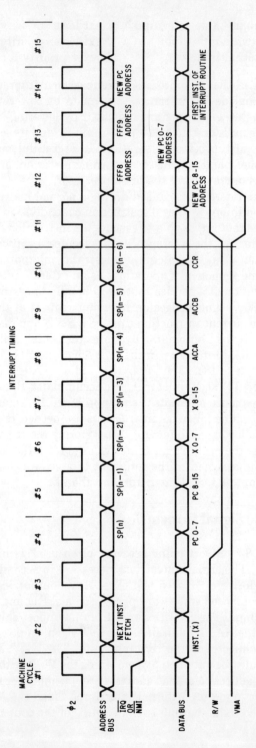

Fig. 5.10 Interrupt processing sequence

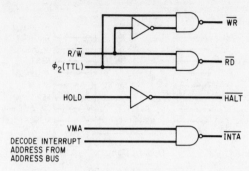

Fig. 5.11 MC6800/8080 signal conversions

dress bus will also be necessary if the input/output ports of the support chips are addressed by device selection numbers.

MC6875 Clock Generator

Since the MC6800 microprocessor is one of the older versions of a microprocessor, it requires a clock generator circuit on a separate chip. Several clock generator chips can be used for this purpose, the most complete one being the MC6875. The pin assignments and signal descriptions of an MC6875 are shown in Fig. 5.12.

The output signals of a crystal oscillator are attached to input lines XTAL1 and XTAL2, respectively. An external clock signal can be introduced through the EXTCLK input line. In this case, the microprocessor system will adapt to the external clock frequency. This frequency must be four times the desired ϕ_1, ϕ_2 clock frequencies. An external asynchronous and imprecise system reset signal (for example, power on) can be introduced through the $\overline{\text{SYSRES}}$ input line. An MC6875 chip converts this into a precise $\overline{\text{RESET}}$ signal for all the chips in the system.

The clock generator outputs NMOS-compatible ϕ_1 and ϕ_2 clock signals for the MC6800 microprocessor. It also outputs a TTL-compatible ϕ_2 clock signal for support devices. The input signal MEMRDY is used by slow memories to stretch the duration of a clock period during a memory access operation by an MC6800 microprocessor. A timing diagram of the sequence of events during a clock period stretch is shown in Fig. 5.13. The slow external memory chip lowers the MEMRDY input signal. Then, when ϕ_1 goes low, ϕ_2 goes high, and MEMRDY is low, the trailing edge of the C*2 signal initiates the clock stretch. The C*2 signal operates at twice the clock frequency. When the memory chip completes its operation, it raises the MEMRDY signal. The next trailing edge of C*2 terminates the clock stretch period and initiates a new clock period with ϕ_1 high and ϕ_2 low.

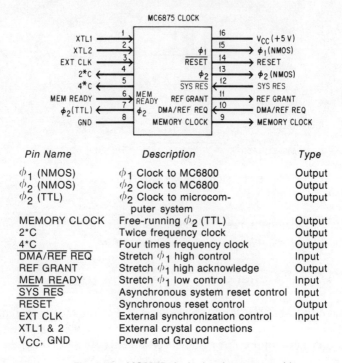

Pin Name	Description	Type
ϕ_1 (NMOS)	ϕ_1 Clock to MC6800	Output
ϕ_2 (NMOS)	ϕ_2 Clock to MC6800	Output
ϕ_2 (TTL)	ϕ_2 Clock to microcomputer system	Output
MEMORY CLOCK	Free-running ϕ_2 (TTL)	Output
2*C	Twice frequency clock	Output
4*C	Four times frequency clock	Output
DMA/REF REQ	Stretch ϕ_1 high control	Input
REF GRANT	Stretch ϕ_1 high acknowledge	Output
MEM READY	Stretch ϕ_1 low control	Input
SYS RES	Asynchronous system reset control	Input
RESET	Synchronous reset control	Output
EXT CLK	External synchronization control	Input
XTL1 & 2	External crystal connections	
V_{CC}, GND	Power and Ground	

Fig. 5.12   MC6875 clock-signal generator chip

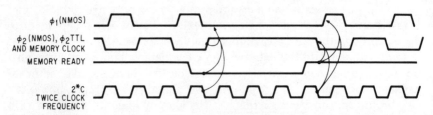

Fig. 5.13   Stretching clock periods by lowering MEMREADY input signal

MC6820 Peripheral Interface Adapter

An MC6820 peripheral interface adapter (PIA) acts as a parallel input/output interface for the MC6800 microprocessor. It has two eight-bit ports through which data can be transferred either in or out of the microprocessor. The ports can be used either as simple input/output ports or in conjunction with a handshaking protocol using interrupt request signals. Neither one of the ports supports bidirectional input/output, but individual lines in a port can be dedicated for either input or output under program control.

PIA Signals and Addressing

The pin assignments and signal descriptions of an MC6820 PIA are shown in Fig. 5.14. The three chip select signals are CS0, CS1, and $\overline{CS2}$. To select a PIA, CS0 and CS1 must be input high and $\overline{CS2}$ input low. Each port of a PIA (called Port A and Port B, respectively) has two control signals. For port A, these are CA1 and CA2. CA1 is normally used by peripheral device controllers to request an interrupt. CA2 is a bidirectional signal used to implement handshaking protocols. CB1 and CB2 have similar interpretations.

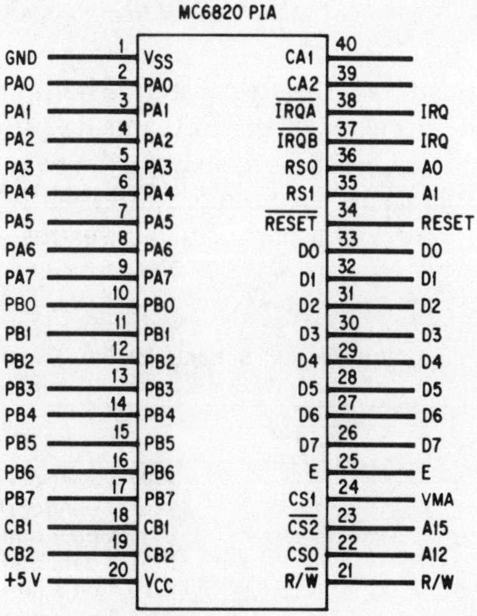

MC6820 PIA

```
GND  ──1── Vss        CA1  ──40──
PA0  ──2── PA0        CA2  ──39──
PA1  ──3── PA1       IRQA  ──38── IRQ
PA2  ──4── PA2       IRQB  ──37── IRQ
PA3  ──5── PA3        RS0  ──36── A0
PA4  ──6── PA4        RS1  ──35── A1
PA5  ──7── PA5      RESET  ──34── RESET
PA6  ──8── PA6         D0  ──33── D0
PA7  ──9── PA7         D1  ──32── D1
PB0  ──10── PB0        D2  ──31── D2
PB1  ──11── PB1        D3  ──30── D3
PB2  ──12── PB2        D4  ──29── D4
PB3  ──13── PB3        D5  ──28── D5
PB4  ──14── PB4        D6  ──27── D6
PB5  ──15── PB5        D7  ──26── D7
PB6  ──16── PB6         E  ──25── E
PB7  ──17── PB7       CS1  ──24── VMA
CB1  ──18── CB1       CS2  ──23── A15
CB2  ──19── CB2       CS0  ──22── A12
+5 V ──20── Vcc      R/W  ──21── R/W
```

Pin Name	Description	Type
D0–D7	Data Bus to CPU	Tristate, bidirectional
PA0–PA7	Port A peripheral Data Bus	Input or output
PB0–PB7	Port B peripheral Data Bus	Tristate, input or output
CS0, CS1, $\overline{CS2}$	Chip Select	Input
RS0, RS1	Register Select	Input
CA1	Interrupt input to Port A	Input
CA2	Port A peripheral control	Input or output
CB1	Interupt input to Port B	Input
CB2	Port B peripheral control	Input or output
E	Device synchronization	Input
$R/\overline{W}$	Read/Write control	Input
$\overline{IRQA}$, $\overline{IRQB}$	Interrupt Request	Output
$\overline{RESET}$	Reset	Input
V_{CC}, V_{SS}	Power and Ground	

Fig. 5.14 MC6820 PIA chip

The input signal E is a device enable signal used mainly to synchronize the internal logic operations of a PIA. This signal can be generated from the ϕ_2 (TTL) clock signal and the VMA, as shown in Fig. 5.15. $R/\overline{W}$ is the read/write signal generated by an MC6800 microprocessor, and $\overline{RESET}$ is a system reset signal.

Each port of a PIA has three registers—(1) the control register, (2) the data direction register, and (3) the data buffer. Input signals RS0 and RS1 are used to address these six registers. However, since the two bits RS0 and RS1 can address only four registers, a special addressing techni-

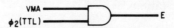

Fig. 5.15 Generation of the E signal from VMA and ϕ_2 (TTL)

que must be used to address the six registers. First, the control register of a port is addressed by means of the RS0 and RS1 lines. Then a control word is written into the control register. At the next access, RS0, RS1, and B2 of the control register are used to address either the data direction register or the data buffer of a port. This addressing scheme is shown in Table 5.1.

Table 5.1 Addressing Scheme for Port Registers

B2	RS1	RS0	Addressed register
X	0	1	Port A control register
X	1	1	Port B control register
0	0	1	Port A data buffer
1	0	1	Port B data buffer
0	0	0	Port A data direction register
1	0	0	Port B data direction register

PIA Operating Modes

The major operating modes of PIA ports are listed in Table 5.2.

Table 5.2 Operating Modes of PIA Ports

Operating mode	PIA port
Simple data input	Port A or B
Simple data output	Port A or B
Data input with handshaking	Port A only
Data output with handshaking	Port B only

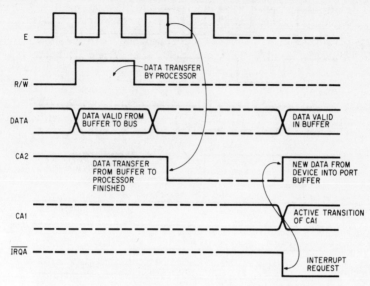

Fig. 5.16 Data input operation with handshaking (PIA port A)

A timing diagram of a data input operation with handshaking is given in Fig. 5.16. Using the R/$\overline{\text{W}}$ signal, an MC6800 reads data from port A's data buffer over the data bus D0, ..., D7. The bidirectional signal CA2 is lowered by the microprocessor at the trailing edge of the next E pulse. This signals the external device controller that data transferred to port A has been read by the microprocessor. Upon transferring new data into port A, the device controller causes an active transition of the CA1 signal. This active transition resets CA2 and generates an interrupt request. The direction of transition of CA1 considered active is defined by bit B1 of the control register of port A.

A timing diagram of a data output operation is shown in Fig. 5.17. The microprocessor transfers data from the data bus into port B's data buffer by lowering the R/$\overline{\text{W}}$ signal. The next trailing edge of the E pulse sets CB2 low. This low value of CB2 signals the external device controller that data is available for output. After data has been transferred out of the data buffer, the device controller causes an active transition of the CB1 signal. This active transition resets CB2 and generates an interrupt request.

PIA Interrupt Handling

The PIA has two output lines, $\overline{\text{IRQA}}$ and $\overline{\text{IRQB}}$, for interrupt requests, one for each port. The conditions at the ports that lead to inter-

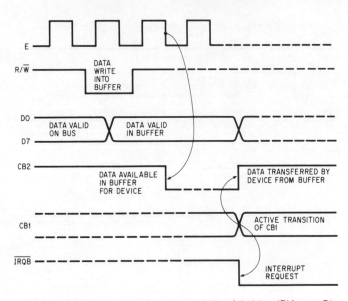

Fig. 5.17 Data output operation with handshaking (PIA port B)

rupt requests can be specified under program control. Each port has two control signals—CA1/CA2 and CB1/CB2, respectively. Normally, interrupt requests are created by active transitions of CA1 and CB1, but they can also be generated by the transitions of CA2 and CB2.

Bit 0 (B0) of the control register disables or enables the interrupt request logic with respect to the transitions of the CA1/CB1 signal. The directions of the active transition of CA1/CB1 are defined by bit 1 (B1) of the control word. Regardless of whether the interrupt logic from CA1/CB1 is disabled or enabled, an active transition of this signal is always recorded as a status by bit 7 (B7) of the control word.

If bit 5 (B5) of the control register is zero, then the interrupt request logic related to the active transitions of CA2/CB2 can be disabled or enabled by bit 3 (B3). In this case, the active transition of CA2/CB2 is defined by B4. An active transition of CA2/CB2 is recorded in B6.

If B5 is 1, then B3 and B4 are used to define automatic handshaking protocols discussed in the previous section. If B5 and B4 are both 1, then CA2/CB2 are set to constant levels defined by B3. These interpretations of the bits of the control register are listed in Table 5.3.

MC6850 Asynchronous Communications Interface Adapter

The asynchronous serial transfers of data between an MC6800 microprocessor and its peripheral device are carried out by means of an MC6850 asynchronous communications interface adapter (ACIA). The

Table 5.3 Settings of the PIA Control Register Bits

Bits	Interpretations
B0	B0 = 0: disable interrupts from CA1/CB1 B0 = 1: enable interrupts from CA1/CB1
B1	B1 = 0: high-to-low transition of CA1/CB1 is active B1 = 1: low-to-high transition of CA1/CB1 is active In either case, record transaction in B7
B2	B2 = 0: RS0 and RS1 select data direction register B2 = 1: RS0 and RS1 select data buffer
B5	B5 = 0: CA2/CB2 allowed to request interrupts B5 = 1: B3, B4 defines handshaking protocol
B3	B5 = 0, B3 = 0: disable interrupts from CA2/CB2 B5 = 0, B3 = 1: enable interrupts from CA2/CB2
B4	B5 = 0, B4 = 0: high-to-low transition of CA2/CB2 is active B5 = 0, B4 = 1: low-to-high transition of CA2/CB2 is active
B3, B4	B5 = 1, B3 = 0, B4 = 0: select handshaking input or output (port A or port B) B5 = 1, B3 = 1, B4 = 0: select simple input/output B5 = 1, B3 = X, B4 = 1: set CA2/CB2 to X

MC6850 ACIA is simple to program but does not offer as many options for data transfer as some other UARTs do. The pin assignments and signal descriptions of an MC6850 ACIA are shown in Fig. 5.18. A functional description of the ACIA appears in Fig. 5.19.

CS0, CS1, and $\overline{CS2}$ are typical chip select signals discussed in previous sections on the PIA. Similarly, the trailing edge of input signal E is used to synchronize internal operations of the ACIA. Two addressable registers are selected by the RS signal after the chip has been selected. When RS is low, a read operation performed by the microprocessor reads the contents of the ACIA status register (see Fig. 5.19), and a write operation writes into the ACIA control register. When RS is high, the microprocessor addresses the ACIA data buffers. $R/\overline{W}$ is the standard read/write signal from the microprocessor. An ACIA has no separate reset signals; it is reset when the microprocessor executes a sequence of instructions designed to carry out a reset operation.

The input signal TCLK is an external clock signal used to time the serial data output operation via the TD line. Similarly, RCLK is used to time the serial data input via the RD line. A single interrupt request line $\overline{IRQ}$ is shared by both the transmitter and the receiver sections of an ACIA. An interrupt service routine, by reading the contents of the status register, determines the origin of an interrupt request. An ACIA has three modem control signals—$\overline{CTS}$ (clear to send), $\overline{RTS}$ (request to send), and $\overline{DCD}$ (data carrier detect). These signals are used to synchronize operations with the external device controllers or modems.

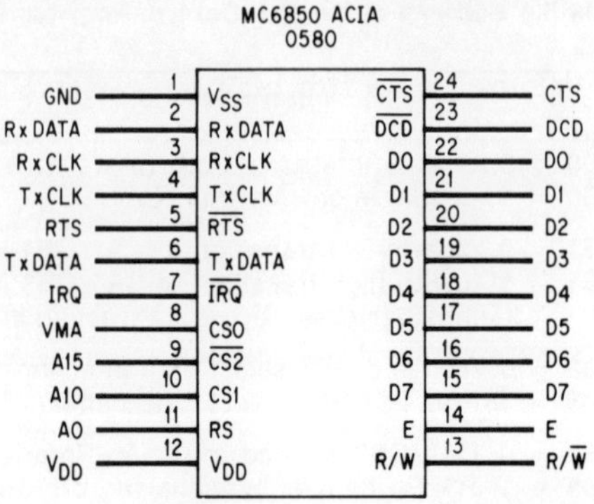

MC6850 ACIA
0580

GND	1 — V$_{SS}$	$\overline{CTS}$ — 24	CTS
R x DATA	2 — R x DATA	$\overline{DCD}$ — 23	DCD
R x CLK	3 — R x CLK	D0 — 22	D0
T x CLK	4 — T x CLK	D1 — 21	D1
RTS	5 — $\overline{RTS}$	D2 — 20	D2
T x DATA	6 — T x DATA	D3 — 19	D3
IRQ	7 — $\overline{IRQ}$	D4 — 18	D4
VMA	8 — CS0	D5 — 17	D5
A15	9 — $\overline{CS2}$	D6 — 16	D6
A10	10 — CS1	D7 — 15	D7
A0	11 — RS	E — 14	E
V$_{DD}$	12 — V$_{DD}$	R/W — 13	R/$\overline{W}$

Pin Name	Description	Type
D0–D7	Data Bus to CPU	Tristate, bidirectional
CS0, CS1, CS2	Chip Select	Input
E	Internal Synchronization	Input
RS	Register Select	Input
R/$\overline{W}$	Read/Write control	Input
TxCLK	Transmit Clock	Input
TxD	Transmit Data	Output
RxCLK	Receive Clock	Input
RxD	Receive Data	Input
$\overline{CTS}$	Clear To Send	Input
$\overline{RTS}$	Request To Send	Output
$\overline{DCD}$	Data Carrier Detect	Input
$\overline{IRQ}$	Interrupt Request	Output
V$_{DD}$, V$_{SS}$	Power and Ground	

Fig. 5.18　MC6850 ACIA chip

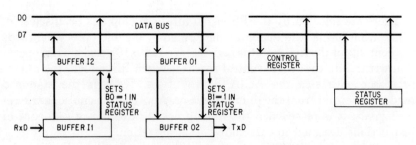

Fig. 5.19　Functional diagram of an ACIA chip

ACIA Operations Control

The serial data transfer operations of an ACIA are controlled by the contents of the control register. Bits B0 and B1 of the control register are used to define the transmitter and receiver clock rates with respect to the data transmission rates specified by TCLK and RCLK. The clock periods of the transmitter and the receiver are usually one-sixteenth or one sixty-fourth of the transmission rate so that the transmitter and receiver can detect the midpoint of a bit period (see Chap. 2). When the transmitter (receiver) clock rate is identical to TCLK (RCLK), it is called an *isosynchronous transmission mode*. B0 and B1 are also used to initiate a master reset by the microprocessor that clears all ACIA registers with the exception of bit 3 of the status register.

B2, B3, and B4 specify the format of serial data transmission. B5 and B6 specify the conditions under which the transmitter can request an interrupt, depending on the level of the $\overline{RTS}$ signal. B7 is used to disable or enable the receiver interrupt request logic. These interpretations of the bits of the control register are listed in Table 5.4.

Table 5.4 Settings of the ACIA Control Register Bits

Bits			Interpretation		
B0, B1			B0 = 0, B1 = 0: isosynchronous transmissions		
			B0 = 1, B1 = 0: 1/16th clock rate		
			B0 = 0, B1 = 1: 1/64th clock rate		
			B0 = 1, B1 = 1: master reset		
B2	B3	B4	Data bits	Parity bit	Stop bits
1	0	0	0	Even	2
1	0	0	7	Odd	2
0	1	0	7	Even	1
1	1	0	7	Odd	1
0	0	1	8	No parity	2
1	0	1	8	No parity	1
0	1	1	8	Even	1
1	1	1	8	Odd	1
B5	B6				
0	0		$\overline{RTS}$ low: disable transmission interrupt		
1	0		$\overline{RTS}$ low; enable transmission interrupt		
0	1		$\overline{RTS}$ high: disable transmission interrupt		
1	1		$\overline{RTS}$ low: disable transmission interrupt; corresponds to output break level		
B7			B7 = 0: disable reception interrupt		
			B7 = 1: enable reception interrupt		

ACIA Interrupt Handling and Status Settings

Various information about interrupt conditions is stored by the ACIA in part of its status register. Thus, status register settings and interrupt handling are discussed concurrently. B0 of the status register is set to 1 when data buffer I2 receives an assembled byte of data from I1.

B0 = 1 creates an interrupt request from the receiver. Whenever data is transferred from buffer O1 to O2, B1 is set to 1, and this can cause an interrupt request from the transmitter.

The value of the B2 bit of the status register is used by the microprocessor to determine the condition of the external device attached to the ACIA. Whenever the data carrier detect signal $\overline{DCD}$ makes a low-to-high transition, an interrupt request is generated, and B2 is set to 1. B2 is reset after the microprocessor has read the contents of the status register and $\overline{DCD}$ has gone low. An interrupt request is generated only by the low-to-high transition of the $\overline{DCD}$ and not by its high state.

Bit B3 reflects the status of the $\overline{CTS}$ control signal. When $\overline{CTS}$ is high, the external device is not ready to receive data. During this period, B1 is kept at zero to inhibit output of new data from the microprocessor.

B4, B5, and B6 are used to indicate the different error conditions that may be encountered in transmission. Whenever an ACIA generates an interrupt request via $\overline{IRQ}$, it sets B7 to 1. By reading the contents of the status register and checking B7, the microprocessor ascertains whether the corresponding ACIA has generated an interrupt request or not. These interpretations of the bits of the status register are listed in Table 5.5.

Table 5.5 Settings of the ACIA Status Register Bits

Bits	Interpretations
B0	B0 = 1: buffer I2 full; request interrupt
B1	B1 = 1: buffer O1 empty; request interrupt
B2	B2 = 1: $\overline{DCD}$ has a low-to-high transition; request interrupt
B3	B3 = 1: external device can't accept data; inhibit B1 (i.e., B1 = 0)
B4	B4 = 1: framing error in transmission
B5	B5 = 1: receiver overrun error; request interrupt
B6	B6 = 1: parity error in transmission
B7	B7 = 1: interrupt request pending via $\overline{IRQ}$

MC6828 Priority Interrupt Controller

In some respects, an MC6828 priority interrupt controller (PIC) is similar to the 8214 PICU of the Intel 8080 family discussed in Chap. 3. The pin assignments and signal descriptions of the MC6828 PIC are shown in Fig. 5.20.

This device receives eight individual interrupt requests on the eight input lines, $\overline{IN0}$, . . . , $\overline{IN7}$. Whenever one or more interrupt requests arrive at the input of a PIC, it generates an interrupt request on its output line $\overline{IRQ}$ and outputs the identification (in binary) of the highest

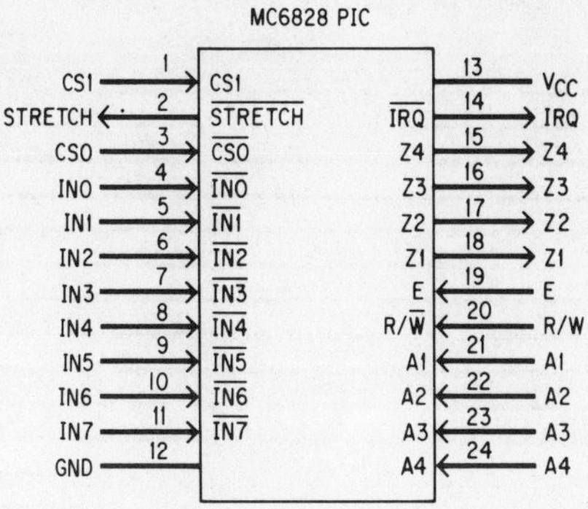

MC6828 PIC

```
          CS1 ──1──▶ CS1        13  V_CC
     STRETCH ◀──2──  STRETCH   ───14──▶ IRQ
          CS0 ──3──▶ CSO    IRQ   Z4 ──15──▶ Z4
          IN0 ──4──▶ IN0        Z3 ──16──▶ Z3
          IN1 ──5──▶ IN1        Z2 ──17──▶ Z2
          IN2 ──6──▶ IN2        Z1 ──18──▶ Z1
          IN3 ──7──▶ IN3         E ──19──▶ E
          IN4 ──8──▶ IN4       R/W ──20──▶ R/W
          IN5 ──9──▶ IN5        A1 ◀──21──  A1
          IN6 ──10──▶ IN6       A2 ◀──22──  A2
          IN7 ──11──▶ IN7       A3 ◀──23──  A3
          GND ──12──            A4 ◀──24──  A4
```

Pin Name	Description	Type
A1–A4	Termination of system Address Bus lines A1–A4	Input
Z1–Z4	Combination of system Address Bus lines A1–A4	Output
IN0–IN7	External Interrupt requests	Input
CS0, CS1	Device Select	Input
R/W	Read/Write control	Input
E	Device Enable	Input
STRETCH	Clock Stretching signal	Output
IRQ	Interrupt Request	Output
V_CC, GND	Power and Ground	

Fig. 5.20 MC6828 PIC chip

priority pending interrupt on output lines $Z1, \ldots, Z4$. The level of priority of the interrupts and the corresponding outputs on $Z1, \ldots, Z4$ are shown in Table 5.6.

Table 5.6 Levels of Priority and Identifications of Interrupts

Priority	Input signal	Z4	Z3	Z2	Z1
7 (Highest)	IN7	1	0	1	1
6	IN6	1	0	1	0
5	IN5	1	0	0	1
4	IN4	1	0	0	0
3	IN3	0	1	1	1
2	IN2	0	1	1	0
1	IN1	0	1	0	1
0 (Lowest)	IN0	0	1	0	0

When an MC6800 microprocessor acknowledges an external interrupt from a peripheral device, it branches to a fixed location in the memory. The MC6828 PIC traps part of the lower byte of this address and replaces it with its output on lines $Z1, \ldots Z4$, as shown in Fig. 5.21. Thus, depending on the bit pattern on the lines, the microprocessor branches to one of eight possible memory locations. This trap is activated only when

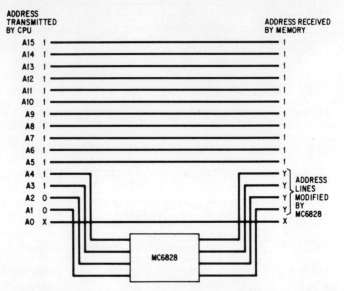

Fig. 5.21 Connection of PIC for trapping interrupt generated addresses

the PIC has been selected by the microprocessor and recognizes part of
the lower byte of the memory address to be an interrupt branch address.
Otherwise, the PIC does not trap any other addresses, that is, the output
on lines $Z1, \ldots, Z4$ reflects the inputs on address lines $A1, \ldots, A4$. In
this manner, the PIC provides the MC6800 with a rudimentary system
for interrupt address vectoring. The address trap is activated whenever
the input signals are $R/\overline{W} = 1$, $\overline{CS0} = 0$, $CS1 = 1$, $A4 = 1$, $A3 = 1$, $A2
= 0$ and $A1 = 0$.

When $R/\overline{W} = 0$, $\overline{CS0} = 0$ and $CS1 = 1$, the PIC is selected but does
not trap the incoming address. It considers the values of A4, A3, A2, and
A1 to define a control word that, in turn, defines the level below which all
interrupts are disabled. This interrupt disabling code is listed in Table
5.7.

Table 5.7 Interrupt Disabling Code

A4	A3	A2	A1	Disable all interrupts including and lower than
0	0	0	0	All interrupts enabled
0	0	0	1	IN1
0	0	1	0	IN2
0	0	1	1	IN3
0	1	0	0	IN4
0	1	0	1	IN5
0	1	1	0	IN6
0	1	1	1	IN7
1	1	1	1	All interrupts disabled

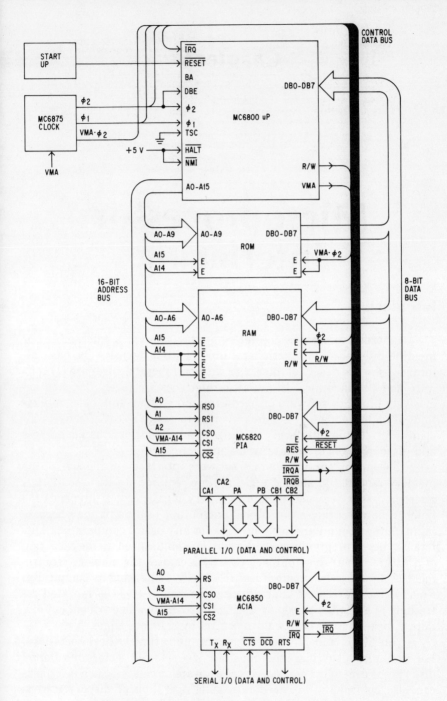

Fig. 5.22 A complete 6800 microcomputer system

A functional diagram of the complete 6800 microcomputer system is shown in Fig. 5.22.

Chapter 6

Microprocessor Interfacing

Introduction

In order to create a useful computing system a microprocessor must be interfaced with peripheral input/output devices. The basic alternatives in the design of interfaces with peripheral devices are (1) software and (2) hardware. In practice, interfaces are rarely designed exclusively of either software or hardware; more often, suitable combinations of both are made. Therefore in order to design a cost-effective, efficient and reliable interface, the designer must consider the advantages and disadvantages of both software and hardware.

The major parameters of a software interface are the size of the memory required to store it and the time required for its execution. A microprocessor does not operate at a very high speed. If it spends too much time executing a complex input/output routine, it may become input/output bound and have no time for any useful computation. Different types of programming tricks can be used to speed up the execution of a program, but this approach usually increases the memory requirement and makes the program less reliable by increasing its complexity. Finally, there are some time-critical operations—such as repeated refreshing of a display screen or storing bit strings as they stream out of a floppy disk—that are difficult to control by software alone.

Hardware is ideally suited for controlling time critical operations. For example, bit strings streaming out of a selected sector on a floppy disk can be controlled and stored in hardware interfaces. Such interfaces can also control the repeated refreshing operation of display screens without any assistance from a microprocessor. Testing of flags and status signals in software wastes a lot of valuable computation time. Such tests can be reduced by providing interrupt signals and carrying out entire handshake protocols (discussed in Chap. 2) in hardware. On the other hand, hardware is considerably more difficult to design and check out. Another important reason for developing programmable logic elements such as microprocessors is to replace difficult to design hardware with software.

A microprocessor can communicate with its peripheral devices by means of many different protocols. The simplest approach is for the microprocessor to check the status of a device periodically until it is ready to communicate. This approach wastes a lot of processing time while the microprocessor executes a status checking loop, waiting for the peripheral device to respond. It may be preferred for its simplicity nevertheless if the microprocessor is dedicated to servicing a single device. An alternative approach is to allow the device to interrupt the microprocessor when it is ready. When the microprocessor acknowledges such an interrupt, it saves the contents of all the registers and then executes a program to service the device. Upon termination of the service program, the microprocessor restores the previous contents of all the registers and continues with execution of the interrupted program. This interrupt protocol has been discussed in detail in Chap. 2. In case of the simultaneous occurrence of more than one interrupt, an interrupt priority control chip can be used (also explained in Chap. 2). Since microprocessors do not have a large number of peripheral devices because of cost considerations, this is perhaps the simplest communication protocol that can be used.

In order to communicate, a microprocessor has to select a particular device among the many interfaced with it. One approach supplies each device with a unique identification number. Every identification number sent via the address bus of the microprocessor is decoded by all devices, but only the device whose identification number matches that sent by the microprocessor responds. This approach necessitates the use of address decoders and identification number generators in the hardware interface of each device. A simpler approach—commonly called the memory-mapped input/output system—is to consider the internal registers of the device interfaces as part of the microprocessor memory. For example, a microprocessor commonly has 16 address lines. If it is using only 32K of memory, the highest-order address bit is always 0 when it addresses the memory containing programs and data. Thus, any address in excess of 32K can be used to identify an internal register of an interface. Whenever the highest order address bit is 1, the address refers to an internal register of an interface and not to a real memory location. Input/output operations can be carried out by the usual memory reference instructions, using any internal register of the microprocessor, not necessarily the accumulator. Memory-mapped input/output simplifies the design of hardware interfaces and input/output software and also speeds up input/output operations.

Universal Asynchronous Receiver Transmitter (UART)

A microcomputer often communicates with peripheral devices that receive and transmit data in a serial mode, that is, one bit at a time. Examples of such devices are remote keyboards, teletypes, industry standard interfaces, cassette recorders, radio transmitters, and modems for interfacing with telephone lines. Since microcomputers commonly use eight-bit bytes as a standard unit of data, it is necessary to go through a parallel-to-serial and serial-to-parallel conversion at the interfaces with these peripheral devices.

Serial data can be transmitted either in a synchronous or asynchronous manner. These two modes of transmission were discussed in Chap. 2. In the synchronous mode, the transmitter transmits a string of characters continuously. If data is not available for transmission, it transmits a string of synchronization characters. The transmitter and the receiver are synchronized so that the receiver knows when to sample an incoming bit. Synchronous transmission systems are fast but also rather complex.

Most serial data transfers between a microcomputer and a peripheral device are carried out in an asynchronous mode, in which the transmitter emits a mark signal when there is no data to be transmitted. The mark is usually represented by a high signal value so that any break in the transmission circuit will be immediately known. When a bit string is ready for transmission, the transmitter sends a zero bit to denote the start of a transmission. This start bit is followed by the bit string representing data, a parity bit, and one or two stop bits. At the end of transmission, the transmitter continues to maintain a high signal value on its output line as a mark.

For reliability in reception, the receiver samples an incoming bit at the midpoint of its duration. In order to locate the midpoint accurately, the receiver must know the exact rate at which the bits are being transmitted. If the transmission rate is constant, then the receiver can use a clock that runs at exactly 16 times the transmission rate to find the midpoint. In many cases, such as with audio cassettes, the transmission rate varies because of the variations in the recorder speed. In such situations, the receiver is not capable of depending on an independent clock and must therefore derive exact timing information from the incoming bit string.

To simplify the design of interfaces between a microprocessor and peripheral devices that operate in a serial mode, asynchronous receiver/transmitter chips, called *UARTs*, are commercially available. These chips consist of two sections, the receiver and the transmitter, each of which can be operated independently of the other.

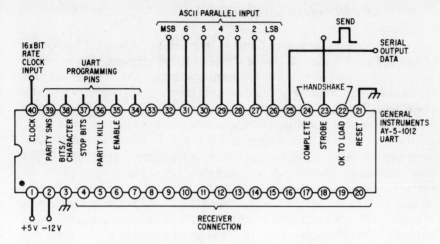

Fig. 6.1 Transmitter section of a typical UART [U1]

UART Transmitter Section

A typical transmitter section of General Instruments' AY-5-1012 UART is shown in Fig. 6.1. It is assumed that the characters being transmitted are coded in the ASCII code, in which seven bits are used to code all characters. These seven bits are obtained from the eight-bit data bus of the microprocessor and applied to pins 26 through 32 of the UART chip. The eighth bit, which is not used in the ASCII code, can be connected to pin 33. A clock signal is supplied through pin 40 to assist the transmitter in maintaining a constant transmission rate. A send command from the microprocessor or a keyboard in pin 23 starts transmission. The serial output of the transmitter comes out of pin 25.

Pins 34 through 39 are used to program the UART for different lengths of bit strings and codes. Pin 34 is an enable signal that is normally set high (+5 V). A parity bit is added in transmission if pin 35 is grounded; otherwise, the parity bit is omitted. Pin 39 is used to select between an even or an odd parity bit. The number of stop bits is selected by pin 36; high provides two stop bits and ground provides one. Pins 37 and 38 together determine the number of data bits to be transmitted, which may vary from five to eight.

UART transmitters are double-buffered so that the next data byte can be accepted as soon as the current data byte is ready for transmission. Pins 22 and 24 are used to provide the handshaking protocol explained in Chap. 2. When pin 22 is high, the next data byte can be loaded into the UART. Pin 24 goes high whenever a data byte transmission is complete.

UART Receiver Section

The receiver section of General Instruments' AY-5-1012 UART is shown in Fig. 6.2. Pins 24 through 39 are used to program the receiver as well as the transmitter. In other words, although the receiver and the transmitter can operate independently, they use the same format for their data. The receiver gets its input bit string via pin 20. The received bits are assembled, stripped of the start and stop bits, and then made available in parallel format via pins 6 through 12. When the data is valid on pins 6 through 12, a high output signal is transferred out of pin 19. The microprocessor, after transferring the data out of pins 6 through 12, returns a completion signal through pin 18, which resets the output signal on pin 19. Unless pin 19 is reset, the UART will fail to output a new character. Pins 18 and 19 can thus be used in a handshaking protocol with the microprocessor. Pins 13, 14, and 15 are used by the UART to signal possible error conditions, such as parity error, framing error, and the like. Pins 4 and 16 can be used to disable the data outputs and the error condition outputs, respectively. The receiver gets its clock signal via pin 17; this signal may either be derived from a clock or obtained from the incoming bit string.

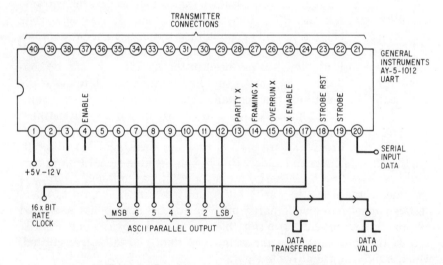

Fig. 6.2   Receiver section of a typical UART [U2]

Direct Memory Access

The handshaking protocol for data transfer discussed so far has used interrupt requests to synchronize data transfer operations. The microprocessor is directly involved in such a data transfer. However, if data is transferred between a RAM chip and one or more peripheral devices, then it seems unreasonable to involve the microprocessor at all. Every time an interrupt request is serviced, moreover, there is a penalty to be paid in wasted time. This is the time used by the microprocessor to save and restore its register contents prior to, and after the completion of, an interrupt service. If large blocks of data bytes are transferred by means of interrupt requests, the microprocessor may have no time left for any other useful computation. The direct memory access (DMA) technique of data transfer provides a means for transferring blocks of data without involving the microprocessor in the transfer process.

To transfer data in or out of a RAM, a device controller needs to control the system bus. An interrupt request from the device controller achieves this indirectly by communicating with the microprocessor, which is in direct control of the system bus. However, when a microprocessor floats a system bus upon request, it is then completely isolated from the support chips that may use the bus. Since the microprocessor is not involved in the operations subsequent to the floating of the bus, it need not save or restore its register contents. It will be ready to continue as soon as the bus is released by the support chips.

The DMA technique is based on the capability of microprocessors to float a system bus. Normally, when a microprocessor floats its system bus, it enters a hold state (8080A or Z-80). To put an 8080A in the hold state, an external device controller raises the HOLD input signal. The microprocessor acknowledges such a hold request by raising the HLDA output signal. In case of a Z-80, a device controller lowers the $\overline{\text{BUSRQ}}$ input signal and the Z-80 enters a hold state by lowering the $\overline{\text{BUSAK}}$ output signal. The timing diagram for this sequence of operations for a Z-80 is shown in Fig. 6.3. The halt state of an MC6800 corresponds to the hold state of an 8080A. For an MC6800, an external device controller lowers the $\overline{\text{HALT}}$ input signal. After floating the system bus, the microprocessor responds by raising the bus available BA signal. When a microprocessor is in a hold state, an external device controller may use one or more machine cycles for transferring data to or from a RAM chip. This mode of operation is called *cycle stealing,* since in effect several machine cycles are stolen from the microprocessor for data input/output operations.

An external device controller that uses the DMA technique is called a DMA controller. In order to transfer blocks of data bytes in and out of a RAM chip, a DMA controller must know the starting address of the block in the RAM and the number of bytes to be transferred. It must also know the direction of data transfer, that is, whether in or out of the RAM. Thus, as shown in Fig. 6.4, a DMA controller will require at least two 16-bit registers. The memory address register initially stores the starting address of the data block in the RAM. Fourteen bits of the second register specify the total number of data bytes to be transferred, and the other two bits specify the direction of data transfer.

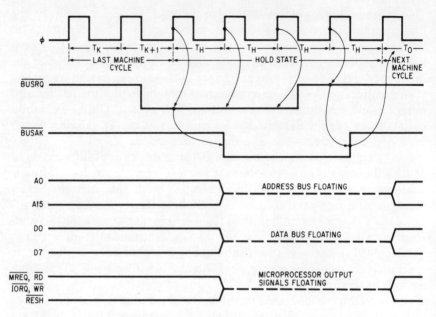

Fig. 6.3 Floating of system bus for DMA by Z-80

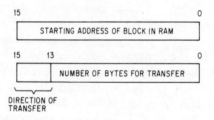

Fig. 6.4 Basic registers of a DMA controller

The following sequence of operations needs to be carried out by a DMA controller to transfer one byte of data. It is assumed that the byte of data is already available for transfer.

1. Transmit a hold request to the microprocessor and wait for an acknowledgement.
2. Upon receiving a hold acknowledgement, put address of memory location on address bus.
3. Put data on data bus if data is being written into the RAM.
4. Send appropriate read or write signal to the RAM.
5. Increment memory address register and decrement data byte counter.
6. Transfer data from the data bus into the data buffer if data is being read out of the RAM.

7. Release system bus and inform the microprocessor.

A DMA data transfer operation is started by a microprocessor under program control. The program provides the starting address of a block in the RAM, the total number of bytes to be transferred, and specifies the direction of transfer. These parameters are loaded into the internal registers of a DMA controller by the microprocessor. From that point on, the DMA controller continues to transfer data by means of cycle stealing. When the byte count reaches zero, the DMA controller signals the end of a block transfer by generating an interrupt request. This sequence of operations is shown in Fig. 6.5.

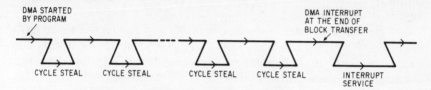

Fig. 6.5 Sequence of operation in block transfer by DMA

Some of the commercially available DMA controller chips can do more than transfer a block of data. They can look for a specific pattern of bits in the byte stream being transferred and signal everytime such a byte is detected. They also allow various modes of DMA transfer, such as the following:

1. Single byte transfer mode, in which each DMA transfers only one byte
2. Burst transfer mode, in which DMA control of the system bus is retained as long as data bytes are ready for transfer
3. Continuous transfer mode, in which, once it is started, system bus control is retained until the completion of the transfer
4. Transparent transfer mode, in which DMA is made during memory refresh operations.

Digital-to-Analog and Analog-to-Digital Converters

The addition of digital-to-analog (DA) and analog-to-digital (AD) conversion capabilities can greatly enhance the usefulness of a home or hobby computer. It should be obvious by now that a microcomputer is inherently a digital device, ideally suited for the control of discrete input and output levels. Many control systems are analog in nature, however, and can be controlled by a microprocessor only when DA and AD interfaces are used. The following sections describe these interfaces.

Digital-to-Analog Converters

Digital-to-analog converters (DACs) are used to convert the digital output of a microprocessor into an analog voltage signal useful to an analog system. There are various hardware techniques (for example, weighted resistor networks) for converting digital signals to analog signals; however, the simplest approach is to use a commercially available DAC chip. Such a chip, Analog Devices' AD7522, is shown in Fig. 6.6. The chip has ten input lines, DB0, . . ., DB9, for accepting ten-bit digital data from a microprocessor. The output currents at IOUT1 and IOUT2 are converted into a voltage signal by means of an M741 operational amplifier. The chip AD7522 is double-buffered; its internal configuration is shown in Fig. 6.7.

The input register of the device consists of two sections—an eight-bit buffer for storing DB0, . . ., DB7 and a two-bit buffer for storing DB8 and DB9. Since most popular microprocessors are eight-bit devices, it requires two transfers to supply all the ten bits needed by the DAC. During the first transfer operation, the least significant bits, DB0, . . .' DB7 are read in from the microprocessor's data bus by means of the LBS signal. During the next transfer operation, the most significant bits, DB8

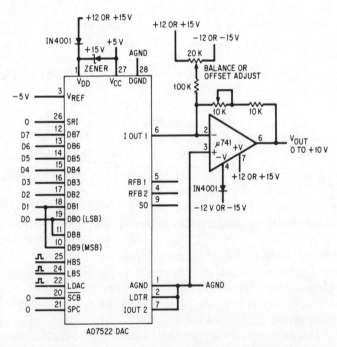

Fig. 6.6 A typical DAC chip (Analog Devices AD7522) [C2]

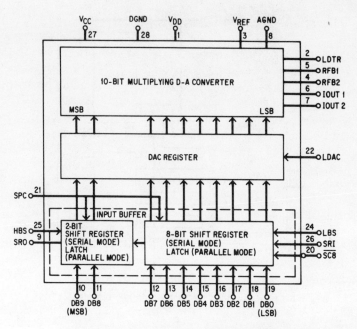

Fig. 6.7 Functional diagram of AD7522 DAC [C2]

and DB9, are read in by the HBS signal. The DB8 and DB9 bits can be obtained from any two lines of the microprocessor's data bus. Mostly for convenience, these bits are obtained from lines D0 and D1, as shown in Fig. 6.6. The LDAC signal is used by the microprocessor for starting the digital-to-analog conversion process. Note that since the input buffer of the DAC is a shift register, it can also be loaded in a bit serial manner.

Analog-to-Digital Converters

A typical analog-to-digital converter (ADC) chip and its interface circuitry is shown in Fig. 6.8. The START signal from the microprocessor to the ADC starts the analog-to-digital conversion process. This conversion process lasts for typically $25\mu s$, at the end of which the digital data are available on output lines D0, . . . , D9. The ADC also generates a DONE signal at the end of the conversion that can be used to interrupt the microprocessor.

Since a microprocessor data bus is normally only eight bits wide, the ten output bits require two transfer operations. Output bits D0, . . . , D9 are stored in two tristate buffers, such as Intel's 8212 chips. The microprocessor enables each buffer chip in sequence and transfers the ten data bits over the data bus in two transfer operations.

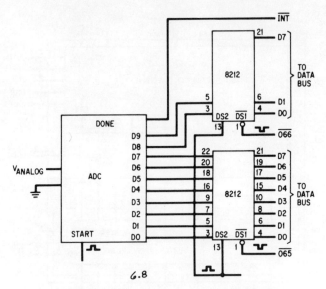

Fig. 6.8　A typical ADC interface with a microprocessor [C1]

Data Transfer Techniques

ADCs and DACs differ from conventional peripheral devices since they are small, fast, and usually located close to the microprocessor. Some of these converters are also buffered, simplifying the process of data transfer with a microprocessor. A DA or AD converter should be addressed as part of main memory (memory-mapped input/output) since they can respond nearly as rapidly as a RAM or ROM. For conversion purposes, this memory-mapped input/output offers the following advantages:

1. Memory reference operations are faster than conventional input/output operations
2. All memory reference instructions are applicable, and data transfer may involve any of the microprocessor's internal registers
3. No separate input/output bus or device selection logic is necessary.

For example, as shown in Fig. 6.9, a 64K memory can be subdivided into 32K of ROM (B15 = 1, B14 = 0), 16K of input/output peripherals such as ADCs and DACs (B15 = 0, B14 = 1), and 16K of RAM (B15 = 0, B14 = 0).

The transfer of data between a microprocessor and its DAC or ADC can be done in one of three possible ways:

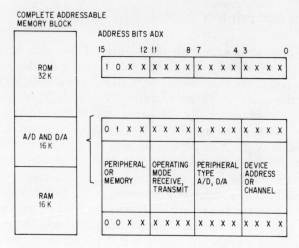

Fig. 6.9 A memory-mapped input/output system [C3]

1. Interrupt controlled transfer
2. Direct memory access (DMA) transfer
3. Auxiliary memory transfer.

In case of the interrupt controlled transfer, the DONE signal from the ADC will interrupt the microprocessor. Since converters are fast devices, this approach will incur considerable overhead as a result of the interrupt processing. Direct memory access allows the converters to operate continuously, and the DONE signal is used to request a cycle-steal operation. However, even a DMA transfer has to use the data bus, and additional hardware is needed to resolve bus contention problems. In the auxiliary memory transfer approach, the converter's input and output data are stored in an auxiliary memory. The microprocessor stores or retrieves blocks of data from the auxiliary memory. This approach frees the microprocessor from constant interference from the converters but requires more sophisticated programming.

No matter which data transfer technique is used, the microprocessor always initiates the conversion operations under program control. The advantages are as follows:

1. Only one instruction is needed to select a converter and initiate a transfer
2. Processor time required is minimal, since a converter needs to be accessed only once
3. Any suitable memory reference instruction can be used
4. No address or data bus switchings are necessary.

Keyboards and Printers

Keyboards are a commonly used means of entering user programs and data into a microcomputer. Coupled with a video display system, the keyboard is one of the most useful input devices available to the microcomputer designer. A large variety of keyboards with different capabilities are commercially available, giving the designer an opportunity to balance cost against performance. On one end of the spectrum are the fully decoded keyboards with built-in interface circuitry. Such keyboards are more expensive but easy to interface to a microcomputer via a parallel input/output port. At the other end of the spectrum are small hex keyboards with no built-in interface circuitry. These are both cheap and practical for entering machine language programs, but they require the design and implementation of interfaces.

In designing a keyboard interface, it is important to realize that a microprocessor is capable of accepting one character at a time at the fastest possible typing rate and still have time to execute other programs. For example, suppose that key strokes are executed at the extremely fast rate of ten per second. A microprocessor executes one instruction on the average of every 5 μs. This rate enables it to execute 20,000 instructions between successive key strokes, more than fast enough to accept a character from the input interface and execute other programs in between.

A functional diagram of a typical keyboard is shown in Fig. 6.10. Depression of a mechanical key generates an eight-bit binary code repre-

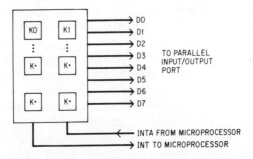

Fig. 6.10 Functional diagram of a keyboard

senting the character on the key on the output lines. A standard binary code used for this purpose is the ASCII, shown in Table 6.1. Not all keyboards use this code, and if a surplus keyboard is used, it may be necessary to change the coding scheme to generate ASCII code.

When a key is pressed down on a keyboard, a unique bit pattern appears on output lines D0, . . . , D7. An interrupt request signal is transmitted to the microprocessor over the INT line. In some cases, particu-

Table 6.1 ASCII Binary Code

Low order bits 3 2 1 0	Hex 0	High order bits 6, 5, 4							
		000	001	010	011	100	101	110	111
		Hex 1							
		0	1	2	3	4	5	6	7
0 0 0 0	0	NUL	DLE	SP	0	@	P	→	p
0 0 0 1	1	SOH	DC1	"!"	1	A	Q	a	q
0 0 1 0	2	STX	DC2	"	2	B	R	b	r
0 0 1 1	3	ETX	DC3	#	3	C	S	c	s
0 1 0 0	4	EOT	DC4	$	4	D	T	d	t
0 1 0 1	5	ENQ	NAK	%	5	E	U	e	u
0 1 1 0	6	ACK	SYN	&	6	F	V	f	v
0 1 1 1	7	BEL	ETB	'	7	G	W	g	w
1 0 0 0	8	BS	CAN	(	8	H	X	h	x
1 0 0 1	9	HT	EM	)	9	I	Y	i	y
1 0 1 0	A	LF	SUB	*	:	J	Z	j	z
1 0 1 1	B	VT	ESC	+	;	K	[	k	{
1 1 0 0	C	FF	FS	,	<	L	\	l	¦
1 1 0 1	D	CR	GS	—	=	M	]	m	}
1 1 1 0	E	SO	RS		>	N	↑	n	~
1 1 1 1	F	SI	US	/	?	O	←	o	DEL

Symbol Identification:

NUL	Null	VT	Vertical Tab	SYN	SYNchronous idle
SOH	STart Of Heading	FF	Form Feed	ETB	End Transmission Block
STX	Start of TeXt	CR	Carriage Return	CAN	CANcel
ETX	End of TeXt	SO	Shift Out	EM	End of Medium
EOT	End Of Transmission	SI	Shift In	SUB	SUBstitute
ENQ	ENQuiry	DLE	Data Link Escape	ESC	ESCape
ACK	ACKnowledge	DC1		FS	File Separator
BEL	BELl	DC2	Peripheral	GS	Group Separator
BS	Back Space	DC3	control	RS	Record Separator
HT	Horizontal Tab	DC4		US	Unit Separator
LF	Line Feed	NAK	Negative AcKnowledge	DEL	DELete (rubout)
		SP	Space		

larly when the keyboard is being used interactively, an acknowledgement signal (INTA) may be sent to reset the keyboard logic.

Basic Features of a Keyboard

When acquiring a keyboard, the operator should look for certain features that eliminate various problems of use. Many of them are standard in well-designed keyboards. The first one to look for is automatic key-rollover protection. A key-rollover problem occurs when a second key is depressed before the current key is released. In an electrical typewriter, the second key stroke is locked out and must be executed again after releasing the current key. A keyboard with automatic key-rollover protection remembers the second keystroke and generates the correct output on the data lines after the initial output is processed by the micro-

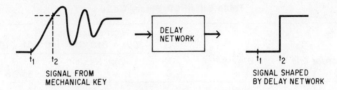

Fig. 6.11   Contact bounce elimination

computer. This feature simplifies typing for persons using more than one finger in quick succession. Note that the problem of key rollover has nothing to do with the speed of execution of the microprocessor.

A delay network to eliminate the effects of contact bounce in mechanically operated keys is another essential feature of all good keyboards. Depression of a key generates the oscillating signal known in Fig. 6.11 as a result of minute variations of pressure on the key and mechanical vibrations. Such a signal is obviously unsuitable for processing by a digital electronic circuit. Since the period of oscillation is much higher compared to the time constants of an electronic circuit, the signal may be erroneously sampled. A delay network generates a sharp and clean signal in response to a keyboard signal, as shown in Fig. 6.11.

Several additional features to look for in a keyboard include N key lockout, self-contained oscillator, static charge protection on all input/output lines, and so forth. It is also necessary to see if the output signals are TTL or MOS compatible. Some commercially available keyboard interface chips have many of these features built into them.

Simple Hex Keyboard Interface

A simple hex keyboard has 16 keys, each of them representing a symbol of the hexadecimal number system shown in Table 6.2. Such a keyboard can be attached to the front panel of a microcomputer as a means of entering short machine language programs. Figure 6.12 shows the interface circuitry for a hex keyboard.

A diode matrix is used to convert the key strokes into unique binary patterns. When a key is pressed, one or more of the encode lines go high, depending on the diode connections. Four encode lines are used to code symbols "1" through "F", and a fifth is used to encode "0". The outputs of the five encode lines are inverted by IC4, and these inverted outputs go low when a key is depressed. The output of IC5 thus goes high whenever a key is depressed.

The transition of the output of IC5 is converted into a positive pulse by the pulse generator and fed to ICs 10A and 10B. One of these two AND gates is enabled by the state of flip-flop IC7. A $\overline{\text{CLEAR}}$ signal from the microprocessor or depression of the clear entry key CE on the

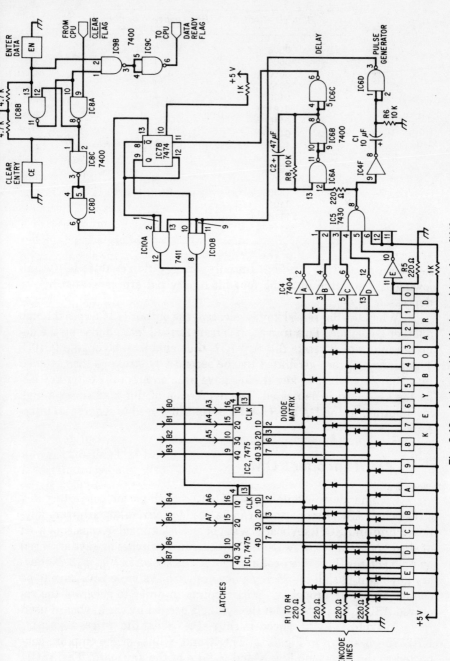

Fig. 6.12 A simple Hex Keyboard interface [K1]

Table 6.2 Hex Keyboard Symbols

Binary pattern	Hex keyboard symbol
0000	0
0001	1
0010	2
0011	3
0100	4
0101	5
0110	6
0111	7
1000	8
1001	9
1010	A
1011	B
1100	C
1101	D
1110	E
1111	F

keyboard resets this flip-flop. Initially, the flip-flop enables IC10A, allowing IC1 to latch onto the four-bit binary pattern generated by the depressed key.

When the depressed key is released, the output of IC5 goes through another transition. This transition is transformed into a pulse by the delay circuit, which resets flip-flop IC7, thus enabling AND gate IC10B. The binary pattern generated by the second key stroke is then latched into IC2. After the two key strokes have been entered, the enter key EN on the keyboard is depressed. The depression of this key causes a high level output on the DATA READY output line used to request an interrupt.

ASCII Encoder ROMs

Commercially available ROM encoder chips for converting key strokes into ASCII bit patterns can be used to convert any arbitrary keyboard into an ASCII keyboard. A keyboard is assumed to consist of a set of single-pole single-throw (SPST) mechanical switches or keys arranged on an eight-row-by-eleven-column matrix, as shown in Fig. 6.13. Not every keyboard has all the 88 keys; however, the available keys have to be connected to the proper X, Y crosspoints in order to generate the required ASCII bit patterns for the symbols needed by the keyboard user.

A typical ROM encoder chip—the Scientific Micro Systems' KR2576—is shown in Fig. 6.14. The X and Y lines of the chip are connected to the corresponding X and Y lines of the keyboard. The ASCII bit pattern for each key symbol appears on D0, . . . , D6. The ROM en-

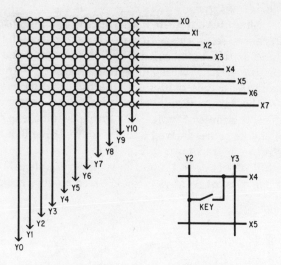

Fig. 6.13 Typical 88 key (SPST) keyboard on an eight-row-by-eleven-column matrix (inset shows a typical key connection)

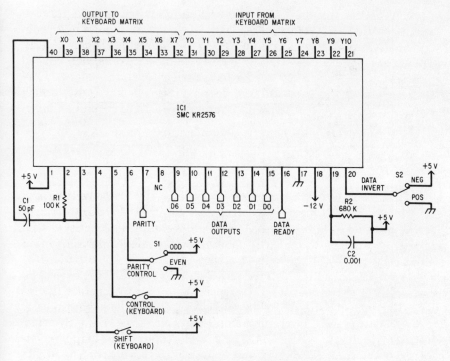

Fig. 6.14 A typical ASCII ROM encoder chip [K2]

coder chip also generates a data-ready signal for the microprocessor and allows the designer to select the parity bit. In order to match the symbols on the keys to their ROM-generated ASCII bit patterns and to connect the keys to the proper X, Y crosspoints, it is necessary to know the relationships among these crosspoints and the bit patterns output by the ROM chip. For the SMC KR2576, these relations are shown in Fig. 6.15. Using this figure, a sample of typical key symbols and the corresponding connection of the keys are derived and shown in Table 6.3. Other standard key connections are shown in Fig. 6.15.

Since a full ASCII code allows 128 symbols (Table 6.1) and a typical keyboard has at most 88 keys (Fig. 6.13), some keys are put to mul-

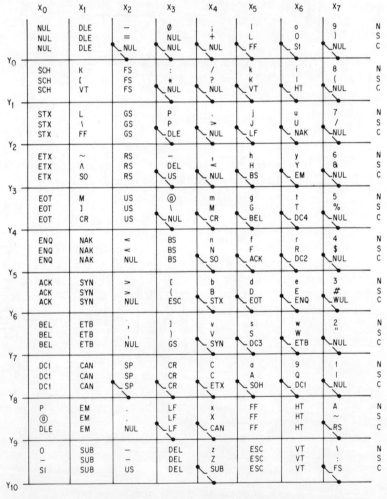

Fig. 6.15 X-Y matrix and ASCII characters of SMC KR2576 encoder [K3]

Table 6.3 Typical Key Symbols and Connections

Key symbols	Key connected to cross-point
a,A,SOH	X5,Y8
b,B,STX	X4,Y6
c,C,ETX	X4,Y8
1,!,NUL	X7,Y8
2,",NUL	X7,Y7
;,+,NUL	X4,Y0
:,*,NUL	X3,Y1
-, =, CR	X2,Y0
CR,CR,CR	X3,Y8

tiple use. The ASCII symbols are partitioned into three groups of 88 symbols each; two special control signals, SHIFT and CONTROL, are used to select the proper partition. When both these control inputs are low, the normal partition is selected. Figure 6.15 shows all three partitions using mnemonics N, S, and C. For example, under normal conditions, the key connected to X5, X9 generates the ASCII code for "a". However, when SHIFT is high, the same key generates the code for "A". Furthermore, when CONTROL is high, the same key generates a control code SOH (start of heading). Thus, by making proper use of SHIFT and CONTROL, the user can generate any of the allowed 128 ASCII symbols when he has 88 keys on his keyboard. It is also clear from Fig. 6.15 that not all 88 keys are necessary to generate all the allowable symbols.

Line printer options

A microcomputer designer must use a line printer whenever hard copies of programs and data are needed. Line printers are also necessary for applications involving the filing of standard forms, such as checks, invoices, and the like. The cost of a line printer depends on the mechanism used for printing, the number of characters printed per line, and the speed of printing. The quality of the printout depends on the type of print mechanism used. The better the quality of the printout and the higher the speed, the more expensive is the line printer.

The most commonly used and least expensive line printers use little print hammers to print dots in a 5×7 dot matrix such as that shown in Fig. 6.16. Seven hammers are moved horizontally across the paper, and at appropriate positions they hit the paper through an inked ribbon. Such printers, called *impact printers,* are useful for making multiple carbon copies. In *nonimpact printers,* on the other hand, the print mechanism does not touch the paper. In *thermal printers,* pulses of heat are shot into special heat-sensitive papers in appropriate dots of dot matrices. *Ink jet printers* shoot little drops of ink onto the appropriate

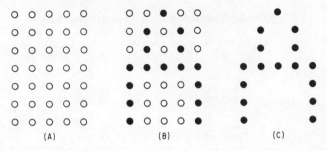

Fig. 6.16 A 5X7 dot matrix print scheme: (a) dot matrix; (b) the character "A" in a dot matrix; (c) actual printout

dots. Nonimpact printers are faster and less noisy than the others but cannot produce multiple copies. The printouts of dot-matrix printers are functional but not very elegant. Printers that use solid characters for printing, like typewriters do, generate more elegant printouts. Such printers use various print mechanisms such as daisy wheels, steel belts, and the like. However, these printers are usually rather bulky and much slower than nonimpact printers.

The number of characters printed per line can vary from 20 to 132, with 80 characters per line the most common. Inexpensive printers print only upper-case letters and lower-case letters must be converted to upper case by the interface circuitry. They also use friction feed mechanisms for advancing paper. Small slippages in friction feeds can cause standard forms to fall out of alignment. Therefore, for printing large numbers of standard forms, such as checks and invoices, printers with more expensive sprocket feeding mechanisms must be used.

Dot Printer Interface

Dot printers with 20 to 80 characters per line are usually not very expensive and are adequate for most microcomputer applications. For that reason, a dot printer interface will be considered in detail. An elegant design of such an interface can be found in the PR-40 dot printer manufactured by the Southwest Technical Products Corporation. The design principles behind this interface are important since they can be used to custom-design interfaces for other dot printers.

The PR-40 is an impact printer that uses a standard 5×7 dot matrix. It prints 64 upper-case ASCII encoded characters with 40 characters per line at a rate of 75 lines per minute. The basic objective of the interface design is to make the printer as independent as possible of the host microcomputer. Figure 6.17 shows the complete interface. The interface stores one complete line of 40 characters in a first-in-first-out (FIFO) buffer memory. A line is printed whenever a carriage return

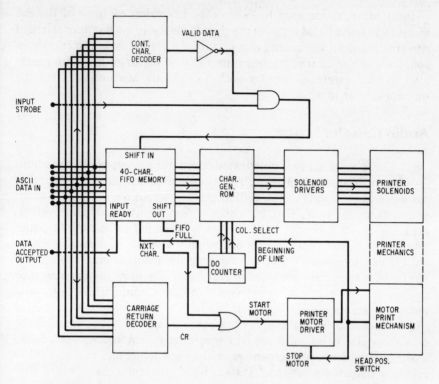

Fig. 6.17 Line printer interface of Southwest Technical Product's PR-40 dot printer [P1]

(CR) control character is received or the buffer becomes full. The alternative approach is to store all the characters in the microcomputer's memory and to transmit one character at a time when the line printer is ready to print that character. This approach obviously requires more software and timing overhead, whereas 40 bytes can be transferred easily via a DMA interface.

The microprocessor transmits ASCII encoded characters over the data lines. A control character decoder circuit decodes and identifies all ASCII control characters. These characters, except CR, are ignored and not stored in the FIFO memory. Whenever a CR code is decoded or a FIFO full signal is received, the print-head motor driver is started up. The print head normally stays in the middle of the page when not in operation. Before starting to print, it travels all the way to the left, changes direction, picks up speed, and starts to move from the left to the right. In the meantime, the paper has been moved up by one line and thus a new line is printed.

The contents of the FIFO memory are transmitted, one byte at a time, to the input terminals of the character generator ROM. The dot counter contents are used to sweep over the seven columns of the dot matrix while the ROM outputs the signals for the print-hammer solenoid drivers. Thus, all the timing and control signals necessary to transfer a complete line of characters from the FIFO to the print head are generated by the interface circuitry with no software instructions from the microprocessor at all.

Audio Cassette System

Every reasonably sophisticated computer system needs a medium for bulk storage of information. This storage medium should be such that storage and retrieval of information can be carried out within a reasonable amount of time, that is, within a few minutes. In many microcomputer systems, such bulk storage is provided by means of paper tapes. The paper tape devices are usually slow in operation, and exchange of information (such as programs) by means of large reels of paper tapes is extremely awkward to carry out. Moreover, many paper tape devices cost as much as, or perhaps more than, some of the faster and more convenient storage systems.

An obvious and extremely low cost medium of bulk storage is the audio cassette commonly used in recording music and speech. Audio cassette recorders are inexpensive, widely available, and can be used to create a potentially low cost system for duplication, distribution, and exchange of programs.

Cassettes and Recorders

Audio cassettes are in such extensive use in everyday life that it is hardly necessary to describe one. It is also unnecessary to know in complete detail the inner workings of an audio cassette recorder. However, certain basic principles must be understood in order to interface these recorders to a microcomputer. An audio cassette records and retrieves information in a serial mode. Moreover, the recorder is an asynchronous device, that is, it does not transmit a continuous stream of synchronization characters when no useful data is available. The basic concepts of asynchronous serial data transmission were discussed in Chap. 2. In asynchronous serial mode, every eight-bit byte of information coming from the microcomputer is stored in a format similar to that shown in Fig. 6.18. The simplest method of interfacing an asynchronous serial transmission device to a microcomputer is by means of a UART, discussed earlier. Among other things, the job of coding and decoding information bytes into designated formats can be easily handled by a UART.

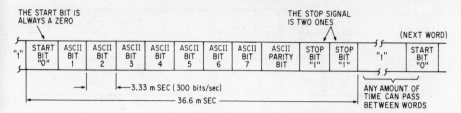

Fig. 6.18 Format of asynchronous serial data

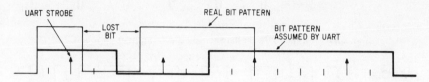

Fig. 6.19 Loss of bit when real bit rate exceeds a rate assumed by UART (transmitted bit pattern 1011; bit pattern recovered by UART 111 or 11?)

For reliability, a UART strobes an incoming bit into its internal buffer at the middle of the duration of that bit. To find this midpoint, the UART must know the exact rate at which the bits are coming in. Figure 6.19 shows a situation in which the real rate of the incoming bits is higher than the rate assumed by the UART, resulting in a loss of incoming bits. The real rate of transmission of bits depends on the speed at which the tape in the cassette is run by the recorder past the read/write head. Unfortunately, in most low- and medium-priced audio cassette recorders, this speed of operation varies over a wide range. Hence, for reliable retrieval of information by a UART from an audio cassette, the interface circuitry must derive the clock signal directly from the tape as it is run by the recorder.

It is also important to realize that digital recording of information on magnetic tape is quite different from the manner in which it is recorded on an audio cassette using an audio cassette recorder. A digital recorder uses pulses of currents in its read/write head that saturate the magnetic tape. Since the signals are binary, there is no need for a "faithful" reproduction of signals with low distortion. The signals in a digital recording system are shown in Fig. 6.20. In an audio cassette recorder, the record and playback circuits operate in a linear manner since low distortion recording and retrieval of signals are important. Digital square wave type signals are not applied directly to the read/write heads. The digital signals received from the UART are filtered by a low-pass filter before recording. Such recorded signals, when played back, are easier to demodulate in the audio receiving circuit. The signals in an audio cassette recorder are shown in Fig. 6.21.

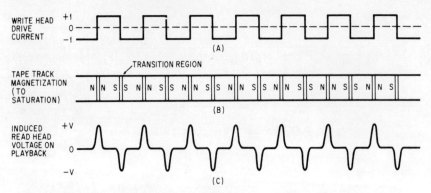

Fig. 6.20 Signals in a digital recording on magnetic tape [AC2]

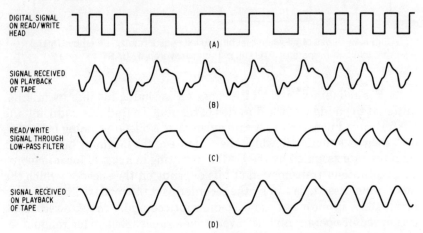

Fig. 6.21 Signals in recording an audio cassette [signal (d) received from tape on playback can be easily demodulated] [AC1]

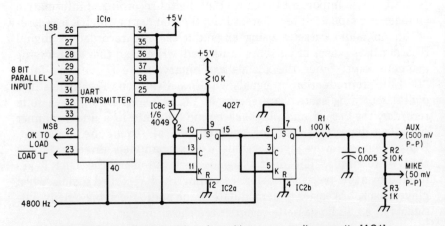

Fig. 6.22 Hardware interface for writing on an audio cassette [AC1]

Although, in principle, any audio cassette recorder can be interfaced with a microcomputer, the cheapest models will not provide a high quality system. The recorder must have an auxiliary or microphone input terminal and an earphone output terminal. Recorders with an ac bias and erase circuit will provide the highest quality recordings. A digital tape counter is also a useful feature to have since it helps in locating segments of information stored on a tape. Only the highest quality audio cassettes should be used for digital information storage.

Cassette Writing Interface

Figure 6.22 shows a hardware interface that can be used for recording digital information on an audio cassette. The digital information from a microcomputer comes in eight-bit bytes. The transmitter section of a UART is used to transform this into a serial string of bits. The serial output of the UART, which is digital in nature, is in the nonreturn-to-zero (NRZ) format, that is, a logical 1 produces a high-level output and a logical 0 produces a low-level output. The output from the UART controls a modulator that has an input signal at a constant 4800 Hz. A crystal oscillator provides the best means for generating this signal. A logical 1 from the UART causes the modulator output to be a signal at 2400 Hz, and a logical 0 generates a 1200-Hz signal. The normal output of the modulator is a string of square waves, although the best signal for audio recording is a sine wave. Since digital generation of sine waves is rather complex, the sharp corners of the square wave are rounded out by the low-pass R1-C1 filter. The auxiliary input of 500 mV peak-to-peak will overdrive a normal microphone input circuit and should be connected only to the auxiliary input of the recorder. The microphone output of 50 mV peak-to-peak is suitable for the microphone input of a cassette recorder.

Cassette Reading Interface

Digital data recorded on an audio cassette, as explained above, has the following format: Logical 1's are represented by a string of approximately sawtooth pulses at 2400 Hz, and logical 0's by a string of similar pulses at 1200 Hz. This type of recording is often called *frequency shift keying* (FSK). The hardware interface for reading such data from an audio cassette and transferring it to a microprocessor is shown in Fig. 6.23. The earphone output of the recorder is passed through an operational amplifier Schmidt trigger (IC3) to a retriggerable oneshot (IC4). The basic period of the oneshot is 555 μs. With a 2400-Hz input signal, the oneshot is constantly retriggered and does not time out. The output of the oneshot sets the IC5a flip-flop to a high state, and this state is in-

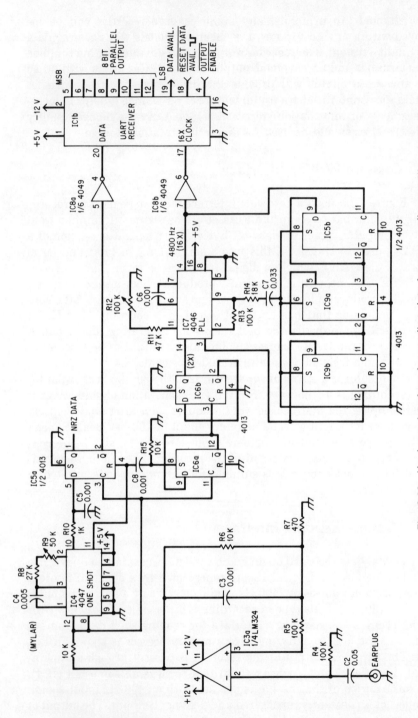

Fig. 6.23 Hardware interface for reading data from an audio cassette [AC1]

terpreted as a logical 1. The period of the 1200-Hz signal is long enough to let the oneshot time out and reset the flip-flop to a low state. This low state is interpreted as a logical 0. The output of this flip-flop is therefore the NRZ serial data recovered from the audio cassette and is fed into the input data terminal of a UART receiver section.

In order to strobe incoming bits, the receiver section of the UART needs a clock signal. Assuming that the incoming bits are arriving at a constant rate (for example, 300 bits/s), this clock signal can be derived from an oscillator. However, due to the variations in speed of the audio cassette drive and the bit rate changes, it is not safe to assume a constant rate. The clock signal for the UART is therefore derived from the recordings on the audio cassette itself by means of IC6a and IC6b.

Every time the 1200-Hz input signal causes the oneshot to time out, IC6a is preset by a pulse generated by C8 and R15. The output of IC6b is then at twice the frequency of the input signal. When the input signal is at 2400 Hz, IC6 acts as a divide-by-four signal generator. The output of IC6 drives a phase locked loop (PLL) oscillator, which runs at 4800 Hz in the absence of any signal. The output of the PLL oscillator provides the clock signal used by the UART to strobe the input bits. The input and output signals of this interface are shown in Fig. 6.24.

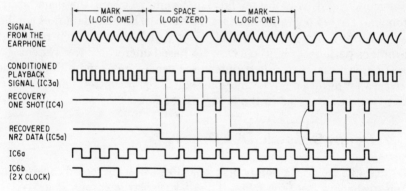

Fig. 6.24 Input and output signals for the interface shown in Fig. 6.23 [AC1]

Floppy Disk System

Direct-access storage devices, such as floppy disks, offer a micro-computer user the potential for a high-performance computer system. Several useful programs can be stored on a single disk. Each program can be listed under a descriptive name, such as EDIT, BASIC, GRAPHICS, and the like, and can be transferred to the random-access memory, ready for execution, by simple commands such as "RUN EDIT". Floppy disks

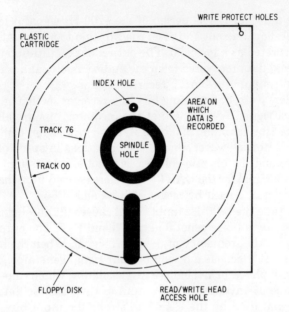

Fig. 6.25   A floppy disk in its 8-inch square protective plastic jacket

also allow rapid assembly of large programs, without the usual start, stop, and rewind operations of cassette devices. Several data files can be merged into a new file on a single floppy disk, an operation requiring several cassette recorders on a cassette-based microcomputer system. To use floppy disks, a microcomputer user needs one or more floppy disk drives, an interface module, and some software for control. These components will be discussed in the following sections.

Floppy Disks and Disk Drives

On the outside, a floppy disk looks like a 45-rpm record enclosed in a plastic jacket (see Fig. 6.25). The disk, constructed out of a Mylar-based magnetic material, is approximately 7.8 in. in diameter, with a spindle hole of 1.5 in. in diameter at the center. The disk is coated with an oxide layer similar to that used on magnetic tapes. Data is stored on the surface of the disk in concentric circles called *tracks*. Floppy disks have either 64 or 77 such tracks, are capable of storing up to 3 million bits, and can transfer data at rates of 250 thousand bits per second (one bit every four microseconds).

Floppy disks are susceptible to contamination by foreign particles such as dirt, dust, and the like. The disks are therefore enclosed in semi-stiff low friction plastic jackets, called *cartridges*. The standard cartridge has three openings in it to allow the spindle, read/write head, and index photosensor to access the disk inside. The index hole is used to synchronize the starting point on tracks with read/write operations. Some cartridges have a small write-protect hole that, when punched out, prevents the writing of new data on the disk. Each track on a disk is organized into sectors for storing data. These sectors can either be defined by software or created in hardware. A hardware-sectored disk has an additional 32 holes in a circle around the spindle to assist the hardware in the detection of sectors. The inside surfaces of a cartridge have built-in, soft, low-friction liners to wipe the disk clean and eliminate static charge. When a floppy disk is not in use, it is normally kept in a cardboard sleeve for storage.

Most floppy disk drives use either a synchronous ac or servocontrolled dc motor to rotate the spindle at 360 rpm. These motors run continuously, and their speed can be accurately controlled—a very important prerequisite for reliable transfer of data. In most systems, the read/write head is moved from track to track by means of a lead screw turned by a stepper motor (see Fig. 6.26). The rotor of a stepper motor turns through a constant angle every time a control pulse is applied to the

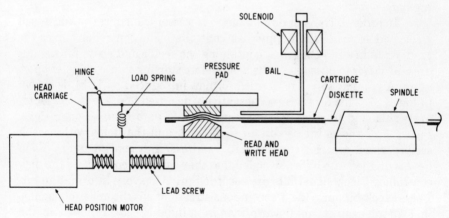

Fig. 6.26 The drive mechanism of a floppy disk system

motor. The position of the head on track 0 is detected by means of a microswitch. Head positioning schemes vary from model to model, and some newer models use coils with linear actuators similar to the acoustic suspensions used in loudspeakers.

Floppy disk read/write heads are contact heads that touch the disk surface to transfer data. Read/write heads on regular disks are suspended by a thin cushion of air that permits higher disk rotational speeds. The chief drawback of a contact head is the mutual wear suffered by the head and the floppy disk. To increase the lifetime of components, most floppy disk drives allow the head to be disengaged from the disk when data transfer is not in progress. Some newer floppy disk systems allow data to be stored on both sides of a disk, and sometimes tracks on each side can be independently accessed.

Information Format on Tracks

Formatting of information on tracks provides a floppy disk controller with its direct-access capability; it assigns addresses to units of data. Formatting can either be assisted by hardware or done entirely in software. In the process of formatting, each track is divided into a fixed number of sectors. Each sector, which is of fixed length, is assigned an address depending on its position on the disk. When formatting is done entirely by software, sector addresses are written at the beginning of each sector. In hardware-sectored floppy disks, each sector is kept track of by means of a series of holes drilled through the disk (not on the tracks). A hardware synchronization circuit uses these holes to latch onto the selected sectors for data transfer. Since the need for storing addresses of sectors on the tracks is eliminated, more space is made available for storing data.

In order to transfer data, a microprocessor transmits the address of a selected sector to the floppy disk controller. The controller moves the read/write head to the track containing the sector and waits for the addressed sector to pass under the head before starting a data transfer operation. A popular software defined format, introduced by IBM, is shown in Fig. 6.27. This format is conservatively designed to prevent accidental overwrites and to simplify synchronization of data transfer operations. Figure 6.27 shows the sectors in each track and the fields within each sector, which are classified as data, address, and control fields. Each field is divided into bytes, so coded that they can be identified by the disk controller. Clock signal bits are recorded prior to every information bit. These clock bits provide a continuous stream of synchronization signals that guard against small variations in spindle speed, although in the process they reduce the number of information bits that can be stored.

The format shown in Fig. 6.27 uses the synchronization pulse created by the index hole as a reference point. Approximately 46 bytes after this synchronization is one byte of *index address mark*, the purpose of which is to inform the controller that the first sector follows after exactly 32 more bytes. Each sector is subdivided into four major fields. The ID field provides a complete identification of the sector. One byte of ID address mark signals the controller to be ready to read the sector address fields. The ID gap acts as a buffer for the following data field and gives the head time to switch to the write mode when data has to be written into a sector. The data field is followed by a DATA gap to guard against data spillover and to give the head time to switch back to the read mode

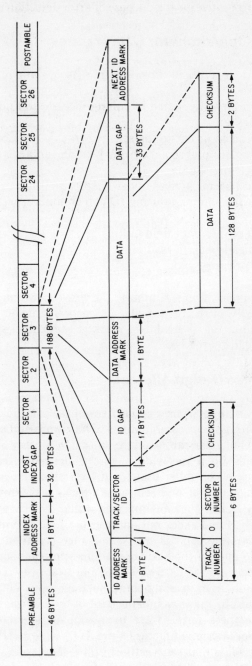

Fig. 6.27 A popular software-controlled format of a track (IBM)

so that the address of the next sector can be read. Various CHECKSUM fields are incorporated for the purpose of error detection in data transfer.

Basic Operations for Data Transfer

The basic operations involved in writing data into a sector are listed below:

1. Decode address specified by microprocessor to find track and sector addresses.
2. Move head in or out to the selected track (0 to 1.5 s seek time).
3. Load pressure pad so as to bring head in contact with track (allow 30 ms settling time).
4. Wait until sector arrives under head (0 to 0.17 s).
5. Issue write command during ID gap or similar presector gap (5 to 10 ms).
6. Write data into data field (10 ms).
7. Switch head back to read mode.
8. Unload pressure pad.

The read operation is similar to the write operation except that the head is normally in the read mode. The actual transfer of data can be started as soon as the data address mark or some other synchronization character is read by the head.

Interface Design Alternatives

A floppy disk interface that carries out the previous operations can be designed with various combinations of hardware and software. An intelligent disk controller can be designed that will carry out all the basic eight operations upon receiving a single command from the microprocessor. Such a controller may even test for errors in transmission, using the checksum bits, and reinitiate a transfer if errors are detected. The only drawback to such an approach is that the complex hardware is difficult to design and check out and can use a large number of chips.

A simpler approach is to use software executed by the microprocessor to do most of the basic operations and leave some of the time-critical operations to the hardware. The hardware can either be custom designed or built from existing chips, such as input/output ports. The hardware should be made as independent of the information formats as possible, since these formats are by no means standard. Nowadays, many microprocessor manufacturers provide programmable floppy disk controller interfaces that can vastly simplify the design problem.

The actual data transfer at a rate of 1 bit per 4 μs is usually too fast for most microprocessors to handle under software control and should be handled by the hardware interface. The software implements the search for the proper track and sector selection operations. The following sections provide the detailed description of an interface designed to operate with a Memorex 651 drive and a Motorola 6800 processor. However, the basic design principles are valid for other systems as well.

A description of the information format is shown in Fig. 6.28. The floppy disk is hardware sectored, and there are 32 physical sectors on each track. The information format uses 16 logical sectors, each sector containing 256 bytes of data instead of 128. This approach allows for future expansion into double-density storage. The hardware interface described below uses no knowledge of the information format; it merely reads or writes a logical sector's worth of bits from the selected sector on the floppy disk.

Hardware Interface

Figure 6.29 shows the schematic diagram of the hardware interface. Signals from the disk drive such as write-protect, file-unsafe, and head-on-track-0 are received by the microprocessor over the data bus (DI-5, . . . ,DI-7) via bus driver IC16s. Microprocessor commands such as step-in, step-out, load-head, and file-unsafe-reset are latched into IC2 and IC20 from the data bus (DO-0, . . . ,DO-7). The sector pulses received from the disk drive are counted by counter IC23, and the output of the counter is transmitted over the data bus (DI-0, . . . ,DI-3). The index pulse is used to clear this counter.

The read and write operations are synchronized by the sector pulses. After receiving the write command, the interface waits till the next sector pulse is detected, the leading edge of which sets a flip-flop (IC30B). This flip-flop generates the write-enable signal through the X-line and remains set throughout the data write operation. It is reset by the leading edge of the next sector pulse. In a similar manner, the reading of data from a sector is started and stopped by the sector pulses.

ICs 4, 14, and 24 in Fig. 6.29 form a random-access 3072-by-1 bit buffer. The addresses of this random-access buffer are generated by the three counters (ICs 5, 15, and 25). While reading data serially from a sector, the SEP CLOCK pulses from the disk drive (see Fig. 6.28) are used to increment these counters. Each bit of data read is stored in an addressable location in the buffer. During a write operation, data are accessed one bit at a time from the buffer and written onto a sector. The necessary clock signals during a write operation are provided by the crystal oscillator. Note that the data to be transferred are stored as a single string of bits in the buffer where each bit can be addressed at random. The microprocessor uses the preset lines of the counter (A0, A1, . . . , A11) to address any bit stored in the buffer. This arrangement al-

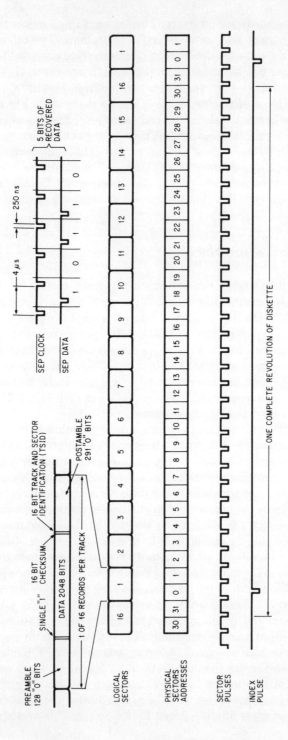

Fig. 6.28 Recording format and timing pulses on the floppy disk [FD2]

lows the hardware interface to be completely independent of the information storage format. The interface simply transfers one sector's worth of bits, the interpretation of this bit string being entirely up to the microprocessor. The three-state bus drivers IC7A and IC7B are used for the reading and writing of single bits into the buffer while IC1 decodes the address of the buffer location supplied by the microprocessor.

During a read operation, the trailing edge of the SEP CLOCK received from the disk drive is used to trigger a one shot (IC22) that generates the necessary write-in-buffer pulse. The data bit received from the sector (SEP DATA) is latched into IC31B and held there until the end of the buffer write operation. Note that the buffer write pulse is also used to change the address of the buffer location by incrementing the counters (ICs 5, 15, and 25) via ICs 13C and 32A. During a write operation, the write clock and write data signals from ICs 17 and 28B are combined and transmitted to the disk drive via three parallel sections of a high-power inverter (ICs 10A, B, and C) to satisfy the current requirement.

Software Interface

The hardware interface shown in Fig. 6.29 is controlled by the microprocessor to execute a disk transfer operation. Since the microprocessor is in charge of operations, operation No. 1 listed in the section, Basic Operations for Data Transfer, is no longer necessary. However operation No. 2, the movement of the head to the desired track, must be carried out in software. Figure 6.30 shows the flowchart of a program used to control the movement of the head.

The Memorex 651 floppy disk has 64 tracks. When the system is turned on, the position of the head is unknown. The disk drive can detect the position of the head only when it is on track 0. Therefore, at the start of operations, it is necessary to move the head outward till it reaches track 0. The track 0 signal is used to clear a register that stores the head position from that point on. Every time the software generates a step-in or step-out pulse for the stepping motor, this register is incremented or decremented by one. The stepping pulse is generated by turning on and then off a hardware bit. Since several instructions have to be executed to do this, the pulse width must be on the order of several microseconds. Successive stepping pulses are suitably separated in time to prevent the stepping motor from overstepping the correct track. Delays for this purpose are introduced by means of no operation instructions (NOPs).

Since counters are used (IC23 in Fig. 6.29) to count the sector pulses, the exact sector number under the read/write head can be read by the software after at most one revolution of the floppy disk. However, the read/write command cannot be issued when the correct sector arrives under the head since by then it will be too late. Also, the counters used

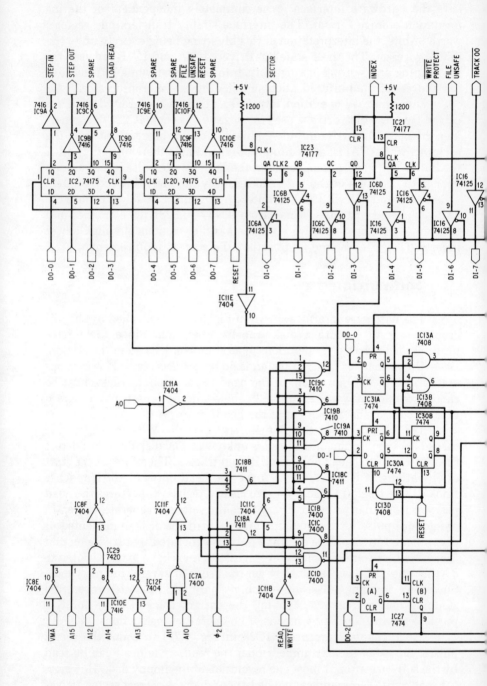

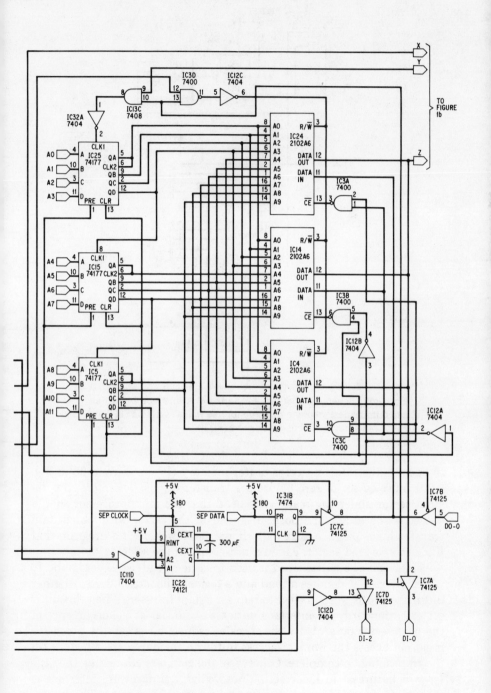

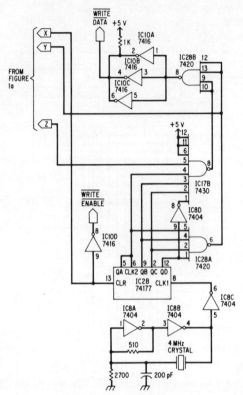

Fig. 6.29 Schematic diagram for floppy disk interface board (all inputs and outputs designed and buffered for use with a Motorola 6800 processor and a Memorex 651 floppy disk drive [FD2])

to address the random-access buffer memory (ICs 5, 15, and 25 in Fig. 6.29) must be set to zero before the transfer begins. Therefore, the desired sector under the read/write head that the microprocessor should detect is the sector one position ahead of the sector with which data transfer takes place. Figure 6.31 shows the flowchart of a program that finds this desired sector, called a *presector,* on the selected track.

One bit of a status word is used to issue a read/write command in which a logical 1 denotes a read and a logical 0 denotes a write. Another bit in the status word is used to request a data transfer. When this bit is set to 1, the hardware interface initiates a transfer at the occurrence of the next sector pulse. Once the transfer request bit is set, the processor must not access the random-access buffer in the hardware interface till the transaction is complete. Otherwise, the counters addressing the buffer will be preset to incorrect values. When the hardware interface is transferring data, it sets a flip-flop to denote a busy state. The micro-

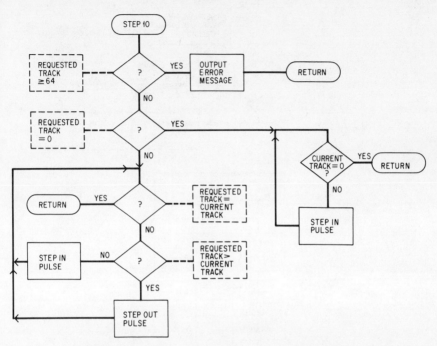

Fig. 6.30 Flowchart of the head positioning routine [FD2]

processor must wait till the busy flip-flop is cleared before accessing the buffer.

Video Display System

All microcomputers need an interface with the human operator. For information input, a keyboard can be interfaced to the computer. For information output, some form of display system is necessary. To create a permanent record, some type of hard-copy terminal must be used. However, since hard copy is usually not needed, the slow speed of operation of a hard-copy terminal becomes a serious bottleneck in the exchange of information. As an alternative means of output, a television set can be interfaced to a microcomputer to display the needed information. Such a system, called a video display system, has a much higher speed of operation and is totally silent in contrast to the noise generated by most hard-copy terminals in operation.

A video display system requires a video display generator, which has to be interfaced to a microcomputer. The generator drives the TV system by either one of two means. It can be connected to a radio frequency modulator whose output can be connected through an impedance

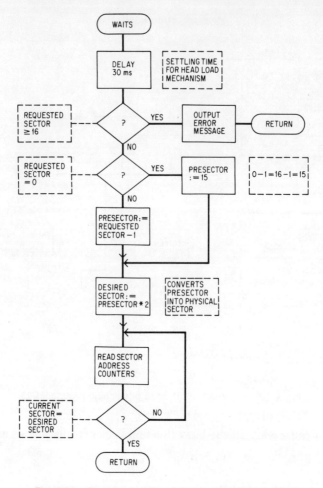

Fig. 6.31 Flowchart of the sector locator routine [FD2]

matching transformer to the antenna terminals of the TV set. This approach allows one to use any available TV set, but such modulators have to satisfy certain FCC regulations. They are also limited in bandwidth, with the result that long lines of characters and high resolution of characters are difficult to implement. The alternative is to connect the video display generator internally to the TV set directly after the video signal detector. To do so, however, requires some modification of the TV set and its dedicated use as a display system for the microcomputer.

Video Display Generator Interface

The functional description of a microcomputer/video-display-generator interface is shown in Fig. 6.32. Most video displays use a 16-line by 32-characters-per-line format on the TV screen. This format requires

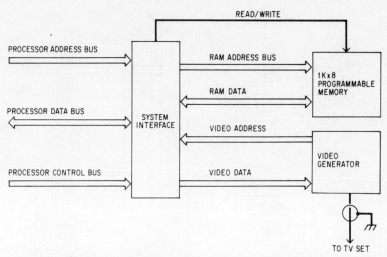

Fig. 6.32 Functional diagram of a microprocessor/video display generator interface [V1]

512 bytes of data stored in a random-access memory. The video display generator operates in a loop and accesses each character in sequence; it constantly displays and refreshes the display on the TV screen. As new characters or lines are created, the microprocessor stores them in their appropriate locations in the shared random-access memory.

The detailed schematic of the interface shown in Fig. 6.32 is given in Fig. 6.33. The interface uses eight $1K \times 1$ bit programmable memory chips (IC 21L-02-1) to store the characters to be displayed on the screen. Except for the data-in and data-out lines, these chips are all connected in parallel and are permanently enabled by grounding the chip select lines. The video display generator accesses these chips at a rate determined by the refresh time requirements of the TV display screen. The address inputs from the display generator are shown at the lower right-hand corner of Fig. 6.33. The output data lines for the display generator are shown at the upper right-hand corner.

The output lines of the memory chips are fed into tristate buffers (ICs 13 and 17) that are connected to the bidirectional data bus of the microprocessor. By enabling these buffers during a read operation, the microprocessor can read the contents of any memory location. The memory chips are addressed both by the video generator and the microprocessor and hence some address switching is necessary. This switching operation is carried out by ICs 14, 15, and 16. When the S input to these chips is high, they connect the lower-order lines of the microprocessor's address bus to the memory address inputs of the memory chips. When S is low, the video generator's address lines are so connected. The S signal of the switching chips is obtained by decoding the higher-order bits on

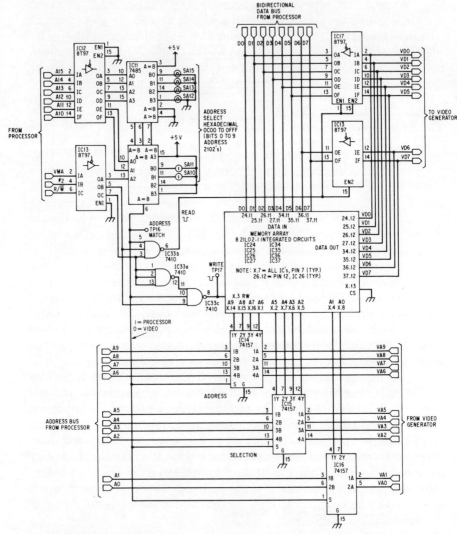

Fig. 6.33 Microprocessor/video generator interface using a random access memory [V1]

the microprocessor's address bus. IC12 and IC13 are permanently enabled tristate buffers that latch these higher-order address bits. These bits, along with the VMA (Valid Memory Address) signal (from a Motorola 6800 processor), are compared by the comparator chips IC11 and IC23 against preset address values. Figure 6.33 shows a scheme that will allow any address in the range OCOO to OFFF to be selected. After the address is stabilized at the address input lines of the memory chips, the ϕ_2 clock pulse transmits the read or write signal to these chips.

While the microprocessor is accessing the random-access memory, the video generator may attempt to access it as well. In this case, the character transmitted to the video generator is the character accessed by the processor and not the one needed by the generator. However, due to the rapidity of the refresh operation and the infrequency of such memory contentions, the rare display of wrong characters is not noticeable.

Graphic Display System

A graphic display system is a logical successor of a video display system. A video display system displays a basic set of characters on a screen; a graphic display system allows the display of lines, pictures, special symbols, and so forth. A graphic display system can therefore be used for such purposes as games, logic diagrams, circuit layouts, special charts, and video art. There are two basic approaches for creating graphic displays. In the *stroke method* of display generation, the following data must be specified to the display generation system: the starting point, the direction of movement, the points at which directions of movement are changed, and the stopping point. The stroke method is useful for displaying curved figures with smooth edges. It cannot be implemented with a standard TV set, however, and it has high bandwidth requirements. It can be more easily implemented with an oscilloscope, although bandwidth limitations can still slow down the refresh rate as more symbols are added to the display, causing a noticeable flicker.

The *dot matrix* method of display generation decomposes the display into a matrix of dots. The total number of dots in the matrix is limited by the size of the memory providing the refresh information. A graphic display system using this method is even simpler to construct than a video display system, since character generators are not necessary and a simple oscilloscope can be used in place of a TV set.

A Graphic Display Interface

If a TV set is used for graphic display, the interface is very similar to that discussed earlier for video display. A much simpler interface will be discussed here that makes use of an oscilloscope and the dot matrix method of display generation. Since most microcomputer designers already possess an oscilloscope for testing, this approach provides an additional use for an existing piece of equipment. This interface is also much simpler and cheaper to construct, allowing one to have a working graphic display system long before a video display system becomes a possibility.

In an oscilloscope, the electron beam normally does not execute a periodic sweep of the display screen. The beam can be moved to any spot

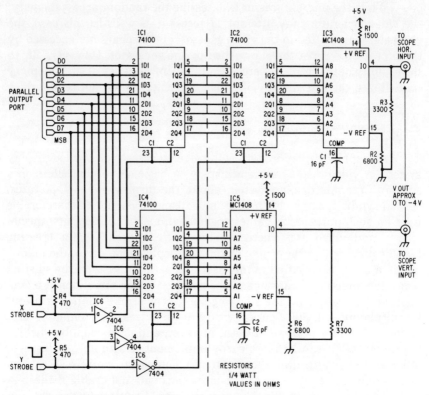

Fig. 6.34 Graphics interface between a microprocessor and an oscilloscope [GP1]

on the screen by applying the proper voltages to the horizontal and vertical input lines of the scope. Thus, any pattern of bright dots can be displayed on the screen by forcing the beam to jump from one dot position to the next with the application of proper voltages to its vertical and horizontal input lines. Such a pattern of dots can be periodically refreshed by forcing the beam to repeat a preassigned set of jumps. As the number of dots on the screen is increased, the time interval between successive refresh operations increases. Thus, an excessive number of dots may cause a noticeable flicker of the image on the screen.

The display screen of an oscilloscope is considered to be a collection of possible dot positions, that is, a dot matrix. A convenient size of this dot matrix consists of 256 rows and 256 columns; the row and column location of any dot in such a matrix can be specified by means of two eight-bit binary words. If it were possible to move the oscilloscope beam by means of direct binary data, then a microcomputer data bus could be directly multiplexed between the horizontal and vertical input lines of the scope. Since this is impossible, the digital position information supplied by a microprocessor is transformed into analog voltage signals by means of digital-to-analog converters (DACs).

The schematic of a graphic display interface, based on the ideas discussed above, is shown in Fig. 6.34. The X-strobe and Y-strobe are used to transfer the column and the row locations of a dot (in eight-bit binary format) from the microprocessor's output port into buffers in the interface (ICs 1 and 4). The X-strobe transfers the column location specified by the microprocessor into IC1. The Y-strobe transfers the row location, similarly specified, into IC4 and the contents of IC1 into IC2. The outputs of IC2 and IC4 are converted by DACs (ICs 3 and 5) and fed to the horizontal and the vertical input lines of the scope. This arrangement causes the beam to jump instantaneously from one specified dot position to the next without sweeping across the screen in successive horizontal and vertical lines. The pictures displayed on the screen are controlled by programs executed by the microprocessor that specify the dot positions that must be illuminated on the screen.

Chapter 7

Selection and Assembly
of
Microcomputers

Introduction

Once a decision has been made to acquire a microcomputer system, the next most important decision is between a fully assembled system versus a system in kit form. The pros and cons of these two alternatives are discussed in the following sections. For each of these alternatives, there are still a large number of systems to choose from. A wrong choice can mean many more hours of extra work and the purchase of equipment not included in the original plan. It is necessary for a beginner to know the task to be completed at each stage of the development of a personal microcomputer system before plunging into the project. A description of these developmental tasks follows.

To Assemble or Not to Assemble

When the major objective is to program a working microcomputer as soon as possible, the proper thing to do is to buy a fully assembled system. This approach frees the user from the complex task of hardware assembly from a kit, but it still may not be simple to run application programs on a fully assembled system. Although a fully assembled system is carefully tested before delivery, it may still fail to operate properly. The user then either has to troubleshoot a system that he does not fully understand or ship it back to the manufacturer and wait. Therefore, unless in a terrible hurry, one ought to consider carefully the advantages of hardware assembly.

Benefits of Using a Kit

Kits are a manufacturer's most economic means for making hardware systems available to users. The labor cost of assembling and testing is eliminated, with a consequent lowering of the system price tag. For users, kits often mean the difference between possessing sophisticated customized systems or conventional ones. Kits have helped to bring personal computer systems within the financial reach of persons of average economic means. Although kits have been a boon to computer manufacturers, their major benefits are obviously for the user who assembles them.

Obviously, assembling a kit can provide one with many hours of exciting challenge and a sense of accomplishment at the end, but the main benefit lies in the learning experience. The process of hardware assembly has an educational impact that cannot be achieved by reading a hundred books. This educational experience is even more important for those with very little background in electronics. Hardware assembly gives them a concrete project to focus their energy and attention on while they are learning something new. One learns something new by the very acts of identifying components, arranging them on a PC board, and finally soldering them on. The learning process may not be obvious, but it is there all the same.

Another major benefit of hardware assembly lies in the training the user receives in maintaining the microcomputer system. No matter how good the hardware components initially are and how carefully they are assembled and tested, eventually some of them will malfunction. A user of preassembled hardware will be at a loss to determine the malfunctioning components. He will have to depend on outside help for troubleshooting, and such help may be expensive and not timely and maybe not even available. It is also possible to make better use of outside help if one knows something about one's own equipment.

Types and Qualities of Kits

Electronic kits can be approximately classified into two groups, (1) those for beginners and (2) those for experts. Beginners' kits are used to build reasonably simple devices such as power supplies and multimeters. These kits come equipped with detailed documentation and instructions for assembly. They also have instructions for testing and troubleshooting the assembled product. Such kits are ideal to start with even though the ultimate goal may be to build a personal microcomputer system. Not only will the experience gained be useful later, but also, if the devices are carefully chosen, they can become a part of the building of a microcomputer system.

Kits for experts are used to build more complex electronic systems such as oscilloscopes, color TVs, and so forth. Such kits are supplied with documentations and instructions just adequate for assembly, but these are often more than sufficient for an expert. A minimum of documentation helps keep the price of such kits within reasonable limits. Unfortunately, most microcomputer kits are of this type, and therefore assembling a microcomputer kit needs careful planning. Assuming that a designer decides to assemble a microcomputer kit, he or she still has a choice among various kits. The qualities to look for in a kit will be discussed next.

Qualities to Look For in a Kit

The design of a kit is its most important quality. A well-designed kit provides a device that is easy to assemble, maintain, and operate. However, the quality of design of a kit cannot be measured by a number. Kits do not come with such a number stamped on them. The only way to ascertain a kit's quality is to talk to owners of such kits and read test reports in computer magazines. Inspection of different kits at a computer store and joining a computer club may also help.

Microcomputer kits vary in the quality of their documentation. Good documentation must not only provide instructions for assembly but also for system start up and troubleshooting. When evaluating the documentation of a kit, ignore books of general descriptions of microcomputers that may be attached to it. Although such books may be useful for general knowledge, they are of little help in assembling a specific kit. Consider only those documents that relate directly to the kit in question and the assembled system. It is a good idea to obtain and analyze the documentations of various kits before purchasing a specific kit.

The quality of the components in a kit is very important for the successful operation of the final product. Kits with commercial components may be more expensive but are more reliable. Surplus or low-quality components may lower the cost of a kit but can lead to system malfunction and long hours of troubleshooting. Support from the manufacturer is also important while assembling a kit. Errors in directions or assembly are always possible, and a manufacturer willing and able to help may mean the difference between a working system and a pile of useless components.

Starting with Kits

A major mistake in assembling a microcomputer from a kit is to rush into the project without adequate preparations. To assemble an electronic kit successfully, it is necessary to have the right kind of tools and some experience with simple kits. The following is a partial list of tools that are absolutely necessary:

1. Screwdrivers of various sizes, including both regular and Phillips types
2. Nut drivers (quarter-inch type, being the most commonly needed)
3. Wire strippers, side cutters, and knife
4. Pliers, especially needle-nose ones
5. Soldering iron, solder, and solder remover

The soldering iron should be of low wattage (25 to 40 W) since excessive heat can damage electronic components. For accuracy, hand-held pencil-type soldering irons are the best. The best solder to use for work with PC boards is rosin core 60-40 type of 0.032-in. diameter. The cleanest way to remove existing solder is by means of solder-removing braids. A certain amount of practice with soldering is necessary before attempting to assemble a microcomputer kit. It may save one from damaging expensive PC boards and chips.

The best way to mount chips on a board is not to solder them but to insert them in sockets. Use of sockets makes it simple to reconnect wrongly connected chips or replace malfunctioning chips. Not all kits supply sockets, and it may be an extra expense. However, in the long run such an extra expense will prove to be well worth it. LSI chips should be handled with care; the pins can easily bend or break, and it is not uncommon to insert them backwards. MOS integrated circuits can be damaged by static electricity from the soldering iron or one's own hand. Sockets can minimize such damage. MOS devices should be left in their conductive foam mat until they are ready to be mounted because the conductive foam shorts out the pins. Prior to mounting the devices, the sockets and the board should be pressed against such a foam mat to keep all the leads shorted. If sockets are used, they should be carefully tested for proper connections. Poor socket connections often cause hard-to-locate system malfunctions.

Reference books and other literature on the operation of microcomputers can be of assistance in understanding a microprocessor kit and its peripheral devices. Such material should be collected and read before one starts a microcomputer kit assembly. Finally, it is always a good idea to start with simpler kits and then gradually move on to kits of higher complexity. If these preliminary kits are chosen with care, then the final assembled products can be used to assist in the assembly of a microcomputer kit. A suggested list of such starting kits includes the following:

1. Power supply with ± 5 V and +12 V outputs
2. Multimeter

3. Prototyping breadboard
4. Crystal oscillator
5. Oscilloscope
6. TV set or TV typewriter

After Assembly, What's Next?

After a microcomputer kit has been assembled and tested and connected to some reasonable peripheral devices such as a keyboard and TV display, what comes next? The designer would like to enter machine language programs from the keyboard into the RAM, but this operation implies that the microprocessor will fetch bytes from its input/output port and write them into the RAM. Without an input/output processing routine to direct it to do so, however, the microprocessor will do no such thing. Thus nothing will happen unless some other means of storing programs in the RAM is used.

If the microcomputer has a front panel, then machine language instructions can be entered manually through the switch settings on this panel. By this means, the microprocessor can be put into a finite loop whereby it fetches a finite number of bytes from the keyboard interface and stores them in the RAM. However, even such a simple set of instructions may consist of several scores of bytes, and it will soon become a tedious process to enter them manually through the front panel. Furthermore, the process has to be repeated every time the microcomputer is powered up.

At this point, the designer usually realizes the great utility of manufacturer-supplied software for the performance of certain basic functions after the system is powered up. Many manufacturers supply complete operating systems in tape cassettes. Such cassettes cannot be read into the RAM, however, unless the microprocessor is capable of supervising its input/output terminals. The best way to incorporate such software into a microcomputer is by means of ROM chips. Storing such basic supervisory software in ROMs has the additional advantages of (1) not requiring reprogramming every time power is turned on, and (2) not getting accidentally overwritten by a user program. Motorola Inc. provides such a ROM-based supervisor, called MIKBUG, for their MC6800 microprocessor systems. This supervisor allows the designer to do the following:

1. Enter programs from a keyboard or tape into the RAM
2. Branch to and execute a program loaded in the RAM
3. Output programs or data from the RAM
4. Examine and/or change the contents of the internal registers of the microprocessor
5. Examine and/or change the contents of specific RAM words

6. Evaluate interrupts
7. Set breakpoints in a user program
8. Load to tape

Hints for Testing and Starting Up a System

With a complex system such as a microcomputer, it is best to interleave the assembly, system test, and start up operations. Errors may occur early in the process of assembly; faulty components may get soldered in. Such problems become difficult to identify and isolate once the entire system has been assembled. Also, start up procedures should be built out of test procedures so that a failure to start up will in most cases provide some clue as to its cause.

First, install all the sockets for the chips and connect them to the power lines. Test each socket to verify that power is available at the specified voltage level. Next, install the clock signal generator chip. With an oscilloscope, verify that all clock signals are properly related in phase and are of the right frequency. Also, verify that clock signals such as ϕ_2 (TTL) are reaching the sockets of all the support chips that need them. Incorrect clock frequency can cause programmable timers to operate improperly.

Before installing the microprocessor chip, check to see if any special reset logic is necessary. If such is the case, then verify that the reset logic is operating correctly. Now turn the power off, install the microprocessor chip, and turn the power back on. Turning power back on should reset the microprocessor. Verify that the microprocessor is transmitting the proper signal levels in its reset mode. Although no memory chips have been installed yet, still it is possible to perform some rudimentary tests. For example, some input signals such as HOLD, $\overline{\text{BUSRQ}}$, and $\overline{\text{HALT}}$ can be set manually and the corresponding output signal settings (HLDA, $\overline{\text{BUSAK}}$, BA, VMA, and the like) verified by tests.

Another possible test consists of connecting the data lines so that a constant object code corresponding to a PUSH or POP stack operation is transmitted to the microprocessor. The output on the address bus should then loop through a sequence of memory addresses that can be detected on a scope. If the signals on any pair of address lines are always the same, this fact indicates a short circuit possibly caused by a solder bridge. If no signals are observed on an address line, it is probably open.

The next stage in the assembly process consists of wiring up the memory board. First, all the sockets are installed and the power availability is verified. Then, the memory board is connected to the address bus and the microprocessor is sequenced through a set of memory addresses. The signals coming through to the address decoder sockets are checked for correctness. Next, the address decoder chips are installed

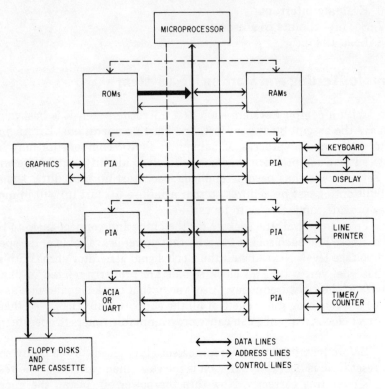

Fig. 7.1 Block diagram of a microcomputer system

and their decoded output signals are tested for proper operation. This includes testing of the chip select lines, which should be active over a fixed period of time. If everything is operational, then power is turned off and the memory chips and the data bus driver chips are installed.

At this point, if a manufacturer-supplied supervisor in a ROM is available, a lot of extra effort can be eliminated. Otherwise, a means must be created, such as a set of toggle switches on a front panel, to load memory manually. Short segments of programs, consisting mostly of branch instructions, should be loaded into memory to form some sort of a loop. The correct execution of such a loop can then be tested by monitoring the outputs on the address and data buses. If this test is successful, then the designer has to assemble the various input/output interfaces, connect them to the device controllers, and test their operations. This process is relatively simple if a ROM-based supervisor is available. Otherwise, at least some simple input/output routines must be written in machine language before even the loading of an assembler can start. This process is quite beyond the scope of a book on hardware. A block diagram of a simple microcomputer system is shown in Fig. 7.1, which the reader can use as a guide to build his own system. Every microcomputer kit should provide a detailed schematic such as that shown in Fig. 7.2. This figure shows a minimal microcomputer system based on an MC6800 suggested by Motorola Inc. It uses two ROM chips (1k by 8 bits each), three RAM chips (128-by-8 bits static memory each), one ACIA, two PIAs, and a clock generator. The ACIA chip can be used as a programmable UART to interface with tape cassettes.

Planning for a Microcomputer System

The entire project of building a microcomputer system can be divided into three parts:
1. Assembling the kit
2. Powering it up and making it operational
3. Writing software

After a kit has been selected, it is necessary to ensure that all the support devices and test tools are available. Assembling a kit without the proper tools can only be an exercise in frustration. Support devices that may be needed are multimeters, oscilloscopes, logic testing devices, and the like. It is not necessary to own all these devices, but some of them at least can be built from kits. If a prototyping breadboard has been built, then the microcomputer should be built and tested on this breadboard before the components are soldered onto the PC board.

The steps necessary to make a microcomputer operational after it has been powered up can be worked out even before the kit is assembled. If the manufacturer does not supply any ROM-based start up routines, then the designer must write at least a simple input/output routine in machine language for a manual start up. The length and complexity of such a routine can be a deciding factor in the selection of a kit.

Finally, the designer should consider the software writing process well in advance of purchasing a kit. It is very difficult to write useful but complex programs entirely in machine language. Sooner or later, the designer has to use either an assembly language or a high-level language. It is wise to plan for such eventualities ahead of time. At an absolute minimum, the designer will need an assembler and a loader. To be able to manipulate and change his programs without too much effort, he will also require the services of an editor. For execution time debugging, it is necessary to have a debugger. Before purchasing a kit, the designer should find out if the kit manufacturer can supply these software development tools. If the manufacturer's software development tools are based on a cross-computer system, then it may be difficult to use them without at least a supporting minicomputer. If the manufacturer provides his software development tools on cassettes, then it will be neces-

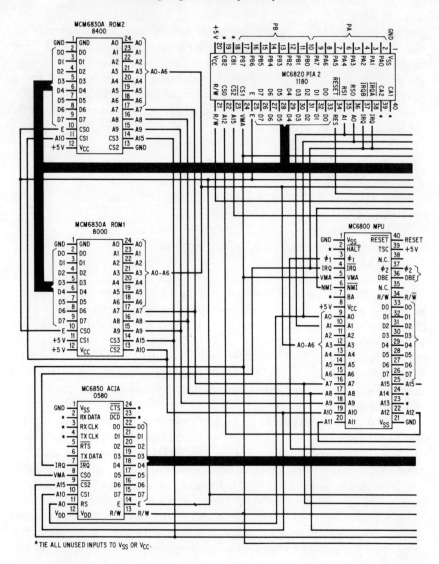

* TIE ALL UNUSED INPUTS TO V$_{SS}$ OR V$_{CC}$.

sary to design a cassette interface for the microcomputer. It is also important to determine the memory requirements of these software tools and compute the cost of RAM chips needed to store them before kit assembly starts.

Selecting Microcomputer Peripherals

Microcomputer peripherals determine to a large extent the ease with which a system can be used. Most peripherals cost at least as much

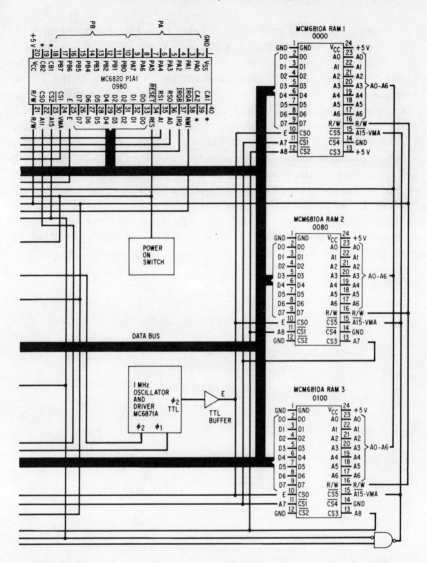

Fig. 7.2 Detailed schematic of a microcomputer based on the Motorola 6800 system

if not more than a microcomputer kit. It is very easy to fall prey to the penny-wise pound-foolish approach when it comes to purchasing them. A simple hex keyboard with a LED display is cheap but totally inadequate for any but toy systems. The designer can save himself money in the long run by carefully evaluating his input/output needs and buying the right peripheral units along with the kit.

With most systems, a full ASCII keyboard becomes necessary in the long run. A TV display unit for outputting short programs and data is also useful. If an RF modulator is used, then the microcomputer interface circuitry can be connected to any TV set while the system is in use. Such modulators must satisfy FCC regulations, however, and be carefully screened. The RF modulator can be dispensed with if a TV set is dedicated for use with the microcomputer. In the long run, such an arrangement is preferable to noisy, slow, and expensive teletype units. If hard copies are absolutely necessary, then line printers may be attached at a later date. The best way to share programs among friends is by means of audio cassettes. Thus, a cassette interface should be included in the initial plan of the system. Since many manufacturers supply software development tools on cassettes, such an interface can be put to multiple use. Other peripheral devices such as floppy disks and graphic displays are optional and can be done without. However, since oscilloscopes are usually available for testing, an inexpensive graphic system can be easily built using it for display, as explained in Chap. 6.

Bibliography

UARTs:

U.1   Lancaster, D., "Serial Interface," *Byte,* Sept., 1975, p. 26.
U.2   McGahee, T., "Save Software: Use a UART for Serial I0," *Byte,* Dec., 1977, p. 164.

Converters:

C.1   Larsen, D.G., Rony, P.R., Titus, C. and J.A., "Microcomputer Interfacing: Interfacing to Analog to Digital Converters," *Computer Design,* Aug., 1977, p. 124.
C.2   ———, "Microcomputer Interfacing: Interfacing a 10-Bit DAC," *Computer Design,* June, 1977, p. 203.
C.3   Schmid, H., and Mrozowski, G., "Mating Microprocessors with Converters," *Electronic Design,* Sept., 1975.
C.4   Carr, J.J., "Interfacing with an Analog World—Part 1," *Byte,* May 1977, p. 56.
C.5   ———, "Interfacing with an Analog World—Part 2," *Byte,* June, 1977, p. 54.
C.6   Bosen, R.J., "Controlling External Devices with Hobbyist Computers," *Byte,* Apr., 1976, p. 42.
C.7   Brown, R., "Building a 12-Bit Analog to Digital Converter for Real Time Problems," *Interface Age,* Feb., 1977, p. 45.
C.8   Hogg, D., "Interfacing the Analog World," *Kilobaud,* Apr., 1977, p. 90.
C.9   Ciarcia, S., "Control the World (Or at best a few Analog Points)," *Byte,* Sept., 1977, p. 30.
C.10   Edelson, R., "Add Analog Capability to Your Computer with the Cromenco D+7A I/O," *Interface Age,* Jul., 1977, p. 59.
C.11   Analog Dialogue, Analog Devices, Nov., No. 1, 1977, p. 14.
C.12   Garen, E.R., et al., "Monolithic Data Conversion Devices, Part 1 and Part 2," *Computer Design,* Mar. and Apr., 1978.
C.13   Zuch, E.L., "Hybrid 12-Bit A/D Converters," *Digital Design,* Mar. 1978, p. 30.

Keyboards:

K.1   Hoegerl, J., "Calculator Keyboard Input for the Micro-
           computer," *Byte,* Feb., 1977, p. 104.
K.2   Brehm, B., "Using a Keyboard ROM," *Byte,* May, 1977, p.
           76.
K.3   Green, S., "A Revision to Using a Keyboard ROM," *Byte,*
           Nov., 1977, p. 164.
K.4   Houser, M., "Keyboard for a 64 Key ASCII Code Features
           Low Power Consumption," *Electronic Design,* No. 4, Jan.
           1977, p. 132.
K.5   Hammond, D., "Chip Scans Keyboard Without Hardware
           Interface," *Electronics,* No. 6, Jan., 1977, p. 110.
K.6   Keppel, M., "Multiplexer Scans Keyboard for Reliable
           Binary Encoding," *Electronics,* No. 17, Mar., 1977, p. 99.
K.7   Sommerfield, "Sophisticating a Surplus Keyboard," *Kilo-
           baud,* Feb., 1977, p. 86.
K.8   Stark, P., "Solving Keyboard Interface Problems . . . Would
           You Believe a UART?" *Kilobaud,* June, 1977, p. 72.
K.9   Brehm, R., "Build Your Own ASCII Keyboard," *Kilobaud,*
           Sept., 1977, p. 22.
K.10   "Keyboards, Review of Available Keyboards," *Digital De-
           sign,* Jan., 1976, p. 61.
K.11   Focus on Keyboards, Runyon, S., ed., *Electronic Design,* No.
           23, Dec., 1972, p. 54.
K.12   King, G., "Keyboards: A State-of-the-Art Survey," *Digital
           Design,* Nov., 1972, p. 20.

Printers:

P.1   Kay, G., "A Review of the SWTPC PR-40 Alphanumeric
           Printer," *Byte,* Mar. 1977, p. 18.
P.2   Simpson, H., "Printers '77 Overview," *Digital Design,* Oct.,
           1977, p. 28.
P.3   Engstrom, P., "Cheap Hardcopy for uP-based systems,"
           Digital Design, May, 1977, p. 68.
P.4   "1977 in Review, Characters and Line Printers," *Digital De-
           sign,* Dec., 1977, p. 42.
P.5   Imbier, E., "A Buyer's Guide to Available Printing Com-
           puter Terminals," *EDN,* Mar., 1977, p. 66.
P.6   Conway, J., "Product Showcase: Computers and Per-
           ipherals," *EDN,* Jul., 1977, p. 114.
P.7   Special Report on Hardcopy Computer Output, *EDN,* Oct.,
           1977, p. 38.
P.8   Bourdeau, D.R., "How to Use the New SWTPC PR-40,"
           Kilobaud, Jan., 1977, p. 104.

P.9   Johnson, L., "Stretch Those Characters . . . Mods for the SWTPC PR-40," *Kilobaud,* Nov., 1977, p. 52.

P.10   Bowers, D., "Technology Profile—Printers and Teleprinters," *Mini-Micro Systems,* Jan., 1977, p. 30.

P.11   Roybal, P., "SC/MP Seiko Printer Interface and Program," *Interface Age,* May, 1977, p. 118.

P.12   Simpson, H., "Printers '77," *Digital Design,* Oct., 1977, p. 28.

P.13   Wieselman, I.L., "Printers," *Mini-Micro Systems,* Jan., 1978, p. 52.

Audio Cassettes:

AC.1   Mauch, H.A., "Digital Data on Cassette Recorders," *Byte,* Mar., 1976, p. 40.

AC.2   Rampil, I., and Breimer, J., "The Digital Cassette Subsystems: Part 1, Digital Recording Background and Head Interface Electronics," *Byte,* Feb., 1977, p. 25.

AC.3   Suding, R., "Build a Fast Cassette Interface," *Byte,* Jul., 1976, p. 46.

AC.4   Rampil, I., and Breimer, J., "The Digital Cassette Subsystem: Part 2, Digital Data Formats and System Considerations," *Byte,* Mar., 1977, p. 38.

AC.5   Kay, G., "The Designer's Eye View of the AC-30," *Byte,* Dec., 1976, p. 98.

AC.6   Hemenway, J., "The Compleat Tape Cassette Interface," *Byte,* Mar., 1976, p. 10.

AC.7   Freeman, W.H., "Cassette Transports for the Roll Your Own Hobbyist," *Byte,* Mar., 1977, p. 26.

AC.8   Liming, G., "Building the AC-30 Cassette Interface," *Byte,* Dec., 1976, p. 110.

AC.9   Johnson, C., "Digital Recording in Low Cost Transports," *Digital Design,* June, 1977, p. 38.

AC.10   King, G., "Cassette, Cartridge and Diskette Drivers," *Digital Design,* June, 1977, p. 50.

AC.11   "1977 in Review: Cartridge and Cassette Drivers," *Digital Design,* Dec., 1977, p. 58.

AC.12   Tuhro, R., "Interface Ties Micro to Standard Cassette Recorder," *EDN,* No. 20, Oct., 1977, p. 110.

AC.13   Adlerstein, S., "Focus on Cassette and Cartridge Recorders," *Electronic Design,* No. 7, June, 1977, p. 66.

AC.14   Childs, A., and Clarke, S., "External Mass Storage . . . Part 2: Digital and Audio Cassette Systems," *Kilobaud,* Mar., 1977, p. 98.

AC.15   Boyle, P., "The Gory Details of Cassette Storage," *Kilobaud,* Mar., 1977, p. 116.

AC.16   Tarbell, D., "Meet the Tarbell/KC Interface," *Kilobaud,* Apr., 1977, p. 44.

AC.17   Mohler, L., "A Clean Cassette . . . Getting the Most from the Inexpensive Recorders," *Kilobaud,* June, 1977, p. 76.

AC.18   McDonough, A.H., and Hammontre, M.P., "Cassette I/O Format . . . Standards Are Still Needed," *Kilobaud,* Aug., 1977, p. 18.

AC.19   "Professional Tips on Cassette Handling," *Personal Computing,* Sept., 1977, p. 124.

AC.20   Stark, C., "Selecting the Best Cassette Tape for Your Recording Needs," *Popular Electronics,* Nov., 1977, p. 47.

AC.21   "Cassette Drives and Systems," Caswell, S.A., ed., *Modern Data,* Oct., 1975, p. 58.

Floppy Disks:

FD.1   Rampil, I., "A Floppy Disk Tutorial," *Byte,* Dec., 1977, p. 24.

FD.2   Allen, D.M., "A Floppy Disk Interface," *Byte,* Jan., 1978, p. 58.

FD.3   Welles, K.B., "Build this Economy Floppy Disk Interface," *Byte,* Feb., 1977, p. 34.

FD.4   Allen, D., "A Minifloppy Interface," *Byte,* Feb., 1978, p. 114.

FD.5   "1977 in Review: Rigid and Floppy Disk Drives," *Digital Design,* Dec., 1977, p. 68.

FD.6   Barnes, D., "Focus on Floppy Disc Drives," *Electronic Design,* No. 11, Oct., 1977, p. 186.

FD.7   Mabon, S., "The New Floppies: Too Little Storage Capacity?," *Interface Age,* Apr., 1977, p. 52.

FD.8   Stevens, R., "PERSCI 1070 Intelligent Floppy Disc Controller," *Interface Age,* Sept., 1977, p. 112.

FD.9   Hogg, D., "Floppy Disks . . . What's the Real Story?" *Kilobaud,* Mar., 1977, p. 70.

FD.10   Shapiro, R., "The Controller: Key to Floppy Disk Performance," *MiniMicro Systems,* Apr., 1977, p. 28.

FD.11   Sollman, G., "A Guide to Floppy Disk Selection," *MiniMicro Systems,* Apr., 1977, p. 36.

FD.12   "Floppy Disk Drives and Systems: Historical Perspective," Bowers, D.M., ed., *MiniMicro Systems, Feb.,* 1977, p. 36.

FD.13   Eidson, M.E., and Parker, L.A., "Synchronous Adapter Reduces Complexity of Floppy Disc Controller," *Computer Design,* Apr., 1977, p. 102.

Video Displays:

V.1   Anderson, A.I., "Build This Video Display Terminal," *Byte,* Nov., 1976, p. 106.

V.2   Lancaster, D., "Television Interface," *Byte,* Oct., 1975, p. 21.

V.3   Gantt, Jr., C.W., "Build a Television Display," *Byte,* June, 1976, p. 16.

V.4   Suding, R., "Build a TV Readout Device for Your Microprocessor," *Byte,* Aug., 1976, p. 66.

V.5   Walters, D.R., "What's in a Video Display Terminal?," *Byte,* Mar., 1976, p. 78.

V.6   Bain, S., "Color Displays on Black and White Television Sets," *Byte,* Feb., 1977, p. 44.

V.7   Lancaster, D., "TV Typewriter Cookbook," *Byte,* Apr., 1977, p. 90.

V.8   Barbier, K., "Some Notes on Building a Display," *Byte,* Jul., 1977, p. 52.

V.9   Wenzhoff, W., "Using the PolyMorphics Video Interface," *Byte,* Dec., 1977, p. 130.

V.10   Processor Technology VDM-1 (Review), *Creative Computing,* Mar., 1977, p. 36.

V.11   Ahl, D., "Some Tips on Using a TV Set for Computer Output," *Creative Computing,* Sept., 1977, p. 32.

V.12   Trottier, L., "Video RAM's Add a New Dimension to Microcomputer Interfacing," *EDN,* No. 5, Mar., 1977, p. 81.

V.13   Latterman, H., "TTL Oscillator Interfaces Data for Display by a Television," *Electronic Design,* Mar., 1977, p. 76.

V.14   Lancaster, D., "A TVT for Your KIM," *Kilobaud,* June, 1977, p. 50.

V.15   Weisbecker, J., "Build the PIXIE Graphics Display, Part IV," *Popular Electronics,* Jul., 1977, p. 41.

V.16   Lancaster, D., "A Low Cost Direct Video Display," *Popular Electronics,* Jul., 1977, p. 47.

V.17   Dash, G., "Build This Video Modulator," *Radio Electronics,* Aug., 1977, p. 33.

Graphics:

GP.1   Nelson, P., "Build the Beer Budget Graphics Interface," *Byte,* Nov., 1976, p. 26.

GP.2   Buschback, T.R., "Add this Graphics Display to Your System," *Byte,* Nov., 1976, p. 32.

GP.3   Deres, Joe, "An Enterprising Display Device (SWTPC GT-6144)," *Byte,* Nov., 1976, p. 42.

GP.4   Lancaster, D., "TV Color Graphics," *Byte,* Feb., 1976, p. 62.

GP.5   Hogenson, J., "Build an Oscilloscope Graphics Interface," *Byte,* Oct., 1976, p. 70.

GP.6   Dwyer, T.A., and Sweer, L., "The Cybernetic Crayon," *Byte,* Dec., 1976, p. 78.

GP.7   Ciarcia, S., "Make Your Next Peripheral a Real Eye Opener," *Byte,* Nov., 1976, p. 78.

GP.8   Antreasian, D., "Graphics Display Adds Versatility to Altair System," *Computer Notes,* June, 1977, p. 8.

GP.9   Pellerin, S., "Graphic Display Systems: Adding Dimension to Computer I/O," *Digital Design,* Jul., 1977, p. 46.

GP.10   Mills, J., "GRAFX: A Graphics Monitor for the 8080/TV Dazzler," *Dr. Dobbs Jour. of Computer. . . ,* Oct., 1977, p. 21.

GP.11   Matic, B., and Trottier, L., "Mate Microprocessor with CRT Displays," *Electronic Design,* Sept., 1977, p. 68.

Microcomputer Assembly:

MA.1   Frenzel, L.E., "What's Involved in Kit Building," *Byte,* Mar., 1977, p.50.

MA.2   Libes, S., "Notes on Bringing up a Microcomputer," *Byte,* Jan., 1978, p. 162.

MA.3   Wyland, D.C., "Design Your Own Microcomputer," *Electronic Design,* Sept., 1975, p. 72.

MA.4   Jones, H.D., "Building a Computer from Scratch," *Byte,* Nov., 1977, p. 80.

MA.5   Brader, D., "A6402 Personal Design: Komputer," *Byte,* Nov., 1977, p. 94.

MA.6   Microcomputer Kits, in *Minimicro Systems,* Dec., 1976.

MA.7   Microprocessor Scorecard, in *Minimicro Systems,* July., 1976.

MA.8   Whitney, J., "Get Your System Together," *Byte,* Dec., 1977, p. 84.

MA.9   "A Note to Novice Kit Builders," *Byte,* Dec., 1977, p. 192.

MA.10   Rampil, I., "One-sided View of Wire Wrap Sockets," *Byte,* Sept., 1977, p. 54.

MA.11   Stetson, R.J., "Design Checklist Aids PC-Board Designers," *Electronics,* No. 18, Aug., 1977, p. 121.

MA.12   Brown, D., "Wire Wrapping," *Kilobaud,* Jan., 1977, p. 64.

MA.13   Young, G., "Getting the Ball Rolling," *Kilobaud,* May, 1977, p. 110.

MA.14   Young, G., "PC Boards and Power Supplies," *Kilobaud,* Sept., 1977, p. 50.

MA.15   Mangieri, A., "Wire Wrapping Techniques for Computer Hobbyists," *Popular Electronics,* Dec., 1977, p. 74.

MA.16   Savage, E., "Extra Hands for the Hobbyist," *Radio Electronics,* Jul., 1977, p. 56.

MA.17   Cardwell, Jr., W., "Construction Technique," *Radio Electronics,* Dec., 1977, p. 58.

MA.18   Hershberger, E., "Space, Order and Good Soldering," *ROM,* Jul., 1977, p. 87.

MA.19   Becker, F., "Tooling Up," *ROM,* Aug., 1977, p. 47.

MA.20   Wood, T., "Helpful Hints or What I Had to Learn to Build a Computer, Nuts and Volts," *SCCS Interface/Microcomputer,* Jan., 1977, p. 50.

MA.21   Wood, T., "Helpful Hints or What I Had to Learn to Build a Computer, Soldering," *SCCS Interface/ Microcomputer,* Aug., 1977, p. 53.

MA.22   Kay, G., "More on the SWTPC 6800 System," *Byte,* Feb., 1976, p. 50.

MA.23   Kay, G., "Build a 6800 System with this Kit," *Byte,* Dec., 1975, p. 72.

MA.24   Abbott, B., "Building a M6800 Microcomputer," *Byte,* June, 1976, p. 40.

MA.25   Zareella, J., "Assembling an Altair 8800," *Byte,* Dec., 1975, p. 78.

MA.26   Gupta, Y.M., "How I Relate to KIM," *Byte,* Aug., 1975, p. 44.

MA.27   Rossi, L., "Homebrew, Custom Designed Computing System," *SCCS Interface/Microcomputer,* Feb., 1977, p. 28.

MA.28   Cushman, R., "Sharpen Your uC Design Skills Quickly on 'uSystem' Projects," *EDN,* No. 20, Feb., 1977, p. 123.

MA.29   Cushman, R., "Even Bare-Bones Development Systems Make Good Learning Tools," *EDN,* No. 20, Mar., 1977, p. 115.

MA.30   Solomon, L., and Viet, S., "Getting Involved with Your Own Computer: A Guide for Beginners," *Interface Age,* Sept., 1977, p. 132.

MA.31   Leventhal, L., "Well, Your Micro's Built. Where Do You Go from Here," *Kilobaud,* Jan., 1977, p. 54.

MA.32   Wozniak, S., "System Description: The Apple II," *Byte,* May, 1977, p. 34.

MA.33   Southwick, D., "Building a Digital Group System," *Interface Age,* Apr., 1977, p. 74.

MA.34   New Hobby Computers You Can Build from a Kit, *Radio Electronics,* Aug., 1977, p. 42.

MA.35   North, S., "How I Built an IMSAI 8080 with Solder, Luck and a Little Help from the Manual," *Creative Computing,* Jan., 1977, p. 30.

MA.36   Stark, P., "Prototyping Systems Exposed! ... A Revealing Look at the Intercept Jr.," *Kilobaud,* May, 1977, p. 66.

MA.37   Loofbourrow, B., "Building the SWTPC 6800," *Creative Computing,* Jan., 1977, p. 33.

MA.38   Berenbon, H., "The Motorola Way ... A Hobbyists Review of the MEK-6800-D1," *Kilobaud,* Mar., 1977, p. 24.

MA.39   Miller, G., "Using a Microprocessor Development System," *Digital Design,* Sept., 1977, p. 101.

MA.40   Stork, L., "Try an 8080 Simulator ... Valuable Debugging Technique," *Kilobaud,* Sept., 1977, p. 64.

MA.41   Maly, R., "Z-80 Development System Disc I/O Keyboard Handler," *Interface Age,* Sept., 1977, p. 167.

Microcomputer Selection:

MS.1   Gray, S.B., "Selecting a Micro," *Creative Computing,* Jul., 1977, p. 31.

MS.2   Purser, R.E., "S-100 Bus Compatible Computer Kits Reference List," *Creative Computing,* Nov., 1977, p. 40.

MS.3   uC Systems Directory, *EDN,* No. 20, Nov., 1977, p. 104.

MS.4   "Product Showcase: Computer System Subassemblies," *EDN,* No. 15, Dec., 1977, p. 208.

MS.5   "Product Guide: Microcomputers," *Interface Age,* Mar., 1977, p. 50.

MS.6   "New Product Guide: Microprocessor Kits," *Interface Age,* Jul., 1977, p. 91.

MS.7   "Basic Guide to Computer Buying," *Popular Electronics,* Dec., 1977, p. 57.

MS.8   "12-Test Benchmark Study Results Show How 3 μp's Stack Up (8080, 6800, 6502)," EDN, No. 20, Nov., 1977, p. 19.

MS.9   Lunch, F., and Showen, C., "Choosing Microprocessors for Reduced Parts Count," *Digital Design,* Nov., 1977, p. 18.

MS.10   "EDN's Fourth Annual Microprocessor Directory," *EDN,* No. 20, Nov., 1977, p. 44.

MS.11   "Microprocessor Selection Guide," *Electronic Design,* No. 11, Oct., 1977, p. 55.

MS.12   "Product Guide: Microprocessors," *Interface Age,* Mar., 1977, p. 48.

MS.13   Raphael, H., "Simplify Low Cost μP Selection," *Electronic Design,* No. 1, Mar., 1977, p. 60.

MS.14   "Choosing a μP by its Capabilities is a Growing 'Family Affair'," *Electronic Design,* No. 5, Jul., 1977, p. 26.

Microprocessor Testing:

MT.1   Holyfield, S., "The Microprocessor Test Quandary," *Electronic Packaging and Production,* Feb., 1976, p. 70.

MT.2   Chiang, A.C.L., and McCaskill, R., "Two New Approaches Simplify Testing of Microprocessors," *Electronics,* Jan., 1976, p. 100.

MT.3   Hnatek, E.R., "Checking Microprocessors?", *Electronic Design,* No. 22, Oct., 1975, p. 102.

MT.4   Alexandridis, N.A., "Bit-Sliced Microprocessor Architecture," *IEEE Computer,* June, 1978, p. 56.

General:

GN.1   Altman, L., "Microcomputer Families Expand," Parts 1 and 2, *Electronics,* Dec. 8, Dec. 22, 1977.

GN.2   Raphael, H.A., "Putting a Microcomputer on a Single Chip," *Computer Design,* Dec., 1976, p. 59.

GN.3   Nichol, J.L., "Hardware Versus Software for Microprocessor I/O," *Computer Design,* Aug., 1976, p. 102.

GN.4   Ciarcia, S., "Memory-Mapped IO," *Byte,* Nov., 1977, p. 10.

GN.5   Raphael, H., "Evaluating a Microcomputer's Input/Output Performance," *Electronics,* Aug., 1976, p. 105.

GN.6   *Creative Computing,* January/February, 1977.

GN.7   *Electronics,* Special Issue, vol. 49, No. 8, Apr., 1976.

GN.8   *INTEL 8080 Microcomputer System Manual,* Intel Corporation, 1975.

GN.9   Suiding, R., "The Circuit for Z-80's," *Byte,* Sept., 1976, p. 62.

GN.10   Hashizume, B., "Microprocessor Update: Zilog Z80," *Byte,* Aug., 1976, p. 34.

GN.11   *M6800 Microcomputer System Design Data,* Motorola Semiconductor Products, Inc., 1976.

GN.12   *M6800 Microprocessor Applications Manual,* Motorola, Inc., 1975.

GN.13   Holt, O., "Microprogrammed Computers," *Interface Age,* June, 1977, p. 56.

GN.14   Ogdin, C., "What Every MICRO Beginner Should Read," *MiniMicro Systems,* May, 1977, p. 80.

GN.15   *MiniMicro Systems,* Nov., 1977.

GN.16   Morgan, C., "The TRS-80: Radio Shack's New Entry into the Personal Computer Market," *Byte,* Nov., 1977, p. 46.

GN.17   "Radio Shack Offers Computer System with Video Display," *Electronics,* No. 18, Aug., 1977, p. 43.

GN.18   Gray, S., "Heath: Two Computers and Two Peripherals for Openers," *Creative Computing,* Jul., 1977, p. 36.

GN.19   Franson, P., "Semiconductors, IC's, Memories and μP's," *EDN,* No. 20, Jul., 1977, p. 70.

GN.20   Nemec, J., and Lau, S., "Bipolar μP's—An Introduction to Architecture and Applications," *EDN,* No. 5, Oct., 1977, p. 79.

GN.21   "Memories and Microcomputers: Technology Update," *Electronics,* No. 27, Oct., 1977, p. 96.

GN.22   Willis, B., "A Primer on Bit Slice Processors, Basics for the Uninitiated," *Electronic Design,* No. 1, Feb., 1977, p. 54.

GN.23   Barden, W., "An In-depth Look at the Z-80," *Radio Electronics,* Nov., 1977, p. 78.

GN.24   Ungermann, R., and Peuto, B., "Get Powerful Microprocessor Performance by Using the Z80," *Electronic Design,* No. 5, Jul., 1977, p. 54.

GN.25   Lau, S., "Design High Performance Processors with Bipolar Bit Slices (3000)," *Electronic Design,* No. 29, Mar., 1977, p. 86.

GN.26   Wilnai, D., and Verhofstbt, P., "One Chip CPU Packs Power of General-Purpose Minicomputers," *Electronics,* No. 23, June, 1977, p. 113.

GN.27   Allison, D., "Small Scale Computing," *IEEE Computer,* Mar., 1977, p. 9.

GN.28   Warren, J., "Personal and Hobby Computing: An Overview," *IEEE Computer,* Mar., 1977, p. 10.

GN.29   Isaacson, P., "Personal Computing Dissected," *IEEE Computer,* Jul., 1977, p. 71.

GN.30   *Zilog Z80 CPU Technical Manual,* Zilog, Inc., 1976.

Appendix A
Glossary of Common Words

access time   The time interval between a request for information from the memory unit and its actual availability to the processing unit.

accumulator   One or more registers for the storage of intermediate results and operands in the arithmetic/logic unit.

ACIA   Asynchronous Communications Interface Adapter; used for interfacing a microprocessor with an asynchronous, serial peripheral device.

address (absolute)   Information used to identify individual storage locations or words in a memory unit.

ALU   Arithmetic and Logic Unit that performs all arithmetic and logic operations in a microprocessor.

architecture   An orderly organization of subsystems to satisfy overall system objectives. *Chip architectures* describe the internal organization of components in microprocessor chips. *System architectures* describe the organization of chips in a microcomputer.

assembler   A computer program that translates assembly language source programs into machine language object programs.

assembly language   A symbolic version of a machine language where operands in the memory unit can be referenced by symbolic addresses in the instructions.

asynchronous operation   A mode of operation of interacting systems in which each system is independent of the internal timing constraints of every other system. For example, the operation of a peripheral device independent of the timing signals that sequence the operations of a microprocessor.

baud   A measure of information flow used in synchronous communication. In digital communication, it is often the same as the number of bits per second transmitted between two systems.

BCD   Binary Coded Decimal; a coding scheme in which every decimal digit from 0 to 9 is represented by its equivalent four-bit binary number.

benchmark   A program used to test and evaluate the performance characteristics of different microprocessors.

bidirectional   A term used to describe signal-transmission lines that can transmit signals in either direction.

binary   A term used to describe the base two number system.

bit   A digit in the binary number system.

bootstrap   A technique for starting up the operations of a microprocessor with a very small program in its memory.

BPS   Bits Per Second; a common measure of the rate of flow of information between digital systems.

branch   An instruction used by a microprocessor to alter the sequence of instructions being executed.

buffer   Storage elements such as registers or memory locations for the temporary storage of information prior to its use by the intended system, such as a peripheral device.

bus   A collection of signal-transmission lines.

bus drivers   Sources of electrical current used to maintain or transmit signals along a bus.

byte   A collection of bits; most often a collection of eight bits as a single unit.

chip   A small piece of semiconductor material containing miniaturized electronic circuits.

clock   A generator of periodic electrical pulses that control the timing of electronic switching circuits in microprocessors. Clocks often derive their basic timing signals from stable crystal oscillators.

CMOS   Complimentary MOS (Metal Oxide Semiconductor) refers to a combination of a p-channel and an n-channel transistor that creates a fast, low-power electronic switch.

compiler   A program for translating high-level language source programs into machine-language object programs.

control bus   That part of a bus used to transmit control and status signals among support chips and a microprocessor.

control register   Registers in interfaces that store control information for peripheral device controllers.

CPU   Central Processing Unit consisting of the ALU, various registers, and control and timing circuits. A microprocessor itself is a CPU of a microcomputer.

CROM   Read-Only Memory used to store the Control programs of microprogrammed microprocessors.

cross-assembler (compiler)   An assembler (compiler) designed for one computer that is executed on another computer.

daisy chain   A chain of support chips connected in a sequence in such a way that a chip enable signal passes from one chip to the next in serial fashion. Any chip receiving the enable signal can trap it and access the bus to which all the chips are connected in parallel. When the enable signal is trapped by a chip, the chips further down the chain do not receive this signal and hence cannot access the bus.

data bus   That part of a bus used to transfer data among the support chips and a microprocessor.

debug   To detect, locate, and correct errors in a program.

dip   Dual in-line package, the container in which a chip resides. The name refers to the double, parallel rows of pins that connect the resident chip to the circuit board.

DMA   Direct Memory Access is a technique for transferring data in or out of the memory unit without disturbing the program being executed by the processing unit. The support chips using DMA steal a machine cycle of the processor and transfer data in or out of the memory using only the memory buffer registers.

editor   A program used to manipulate a source program in an interactive manner.

emulate   To create the machine language instructions of one processor for another by means of microprogramming.

execution time   Time required by a microprocessor to execute a machine-language instruction. The execution time varies from instruction to instruction.

fetch   To obtain or secure information from a memory unit. The information fetched can be either an instruction or an operand.

flag bit   A single bit, stored in a flip-flop, that indicates one of two mutually exclusive conditions or states of a system.

handshaking   A colloquial term that describes a method of data transfer among asynchronous devices, such as a microprocessor and a peripheral device. This transfer involves the use of the interrupt and the interrupt acknowledgement signals.

hard-wired logic   Logic design that uses a number of nonprogrammable LSI or MSI chips as the logic elements.

high-level language   A problem-oriented programming language, closely related to a natural language such as English, that does not reflect the detailed nature of machine-language instructions.

IC   Integrated Circuit; complex electronic circuits fabricated on a single piece of semiconductor material.

instruction register   A register in the microprocessor that stores the current instruction being executed.

instruction set   The set of all machine-language instructions, which can be executed by direct interpretation by a microprocessor.

interface   A common boundary between two systems across which information is exchanged. For example, input/output ports act as interfaces between a microprocessor chip and its peripheral devices.

interrupt   To suspend execution of the current program on a microprocessor in order to service one or more peripheral devices.

I/O   Abbreviation often used for input/output.

jump   See *Branch.*

LIFO   Last-In-First-Out buffer where the last piece of information stored is accessed first.

looping   Executing a fixed set of instructions over and over.

LSI   Large Scale Integration; a technique for fabricating a large number of integrated electronic circuits on a small piece of semiconductor material.

machine language   A format for coding instructions in a binary code that can be directly interpreted by a microprocessor without any further translation.

mask bit   A bit stored in a flip-flop used to cover up or disable some condition, for example, the use of a mask bit to cover up the presence of an interrupt signal.

memory unit   The part of a computer that stores information such as instructions and operands.

microprogram   A sequence of microinstructions that can be directly related to the very basic operations (below the machine language instruction level) of a processor.

MOS   Metal Oxide Semiconductor; a technique for manufacturing field-effect transistors in which the flow of charge inside a semiconductor material is controlled by means of the electrical potentials of metal electrodes attached to the surface.

microprocessor   Central Processing Units built into chips by means of LSI technology.

multiplexing   Distributing and sharing a common resource, such as a bus, among different users.

NMOS (N-channel MOS)   Same as MOS except that the majority carriers in the semiconductor material are negatively charged.

object program   A program written in a machine language.

operand   Data operated on arithmetically or logically by a processor.

overflow   A situation in which the computed result stored in a register is incorrect for any one of many reasons. One common reason for an overflow is that the computed result is too large for storage in a single register.

opcode   A binary code used to identify machine-language instructions. Varies from one processor to another.

PICU   Priority Interrupt Control Unit, a device that arbitrates the priority of simultaneous interrupt requests.

PIO   Programmable Parallel Input/Output interface circuitry.

PMOS (P-channel MOS)   Same as MOS except that the majority carriers in the semiconductor material are positively charged.

polling   A technique for identifying the source of an interrupt signal.

port   A chip through which peripheral devices are connected to a microprocessor.

priority   Refers to a precedence relation applied to simultaneously occurring interrupt signals.

program counter   Register in a microprocessor that stores the address of the next instruction to be executed.

PROM   A read-only memory whose contents can be specified after fabrication, called a Programmable Read-Only Memory.

RAM   Random Access Memory; access time is independent of the location in memory accessed.

real time operation   An operation in which a microprocessor, interacting with an external process, executes its program concurrently with the evolution of the external process.

register   Fast temporary-storage locations, usually inside the microprocessor itself.

ROM   Read-Only Memory; information stored in a ROM is specified during fabrication. This information can be accessed by a microprocessor but cannot be changed.

simulator   A program that simulates a microprocessor on a different computer.

software   A comprehensive set of computer programs and associated documentation.

stack   See LIFO.

stack pointer   A register that always stores the memory address of the top (last-in) element of a stack in memory.

UART   Universal Asynchronous Receiver Transmitter used by a processor to communicate with a device using a serial data format.

vectored interrupt   A technique of interrupt processing in which each interrupt specifies the address of the first instruction of its service routine.

Appendix B
Partial List of Vendors

1. Adaptive Systems
   P. O. Box 1481
   Pompano Beach, FL 33061

2. Advanced Memory Systems
   1275 Hammerwood
   Sunnyvale, CA 94086

3. Advanced Micro Devices
   901 Thompson Rd.
   Sunnyvale, CA 94086

4. AEG-Telefunken
   6 Frankfurt 70
   AEG-Hochhaus, GERMANY

5. American Microsystems, Inc.
   3800 Homestead Rd.
   Santa Clara, CA 95051

6. Applied Computing Technology
   17961 Sky Park Circle
   Irvine, CA 92707

7. Burroughs
   P.O. Box 517
   Paoli, PA 19301

8. Computer Automation, Inc.
   18651 VonKarman Ave.
   Irvine, CA 92764

9. Comstar Corp.
   7413 Washington
   S. Minn., MN 55435

10. Control Logic Inc.
    9 Techn. Circ.
    Natick, MA 01760

11. Data Architects, Inc.
    460 Totten Pond Rd.
    Waltham, MA 02154

12. Data Works
    9748 Cozycroft Ave.
    Chatsworth, CA 91311

13. Digital Equipment Corp.
    One Iron Way
    Marlborough, MA 01720

14. Digital Laboratories
    377 Putnam Ave.
    Cambridge, MA 02139

15. Dynamic Data Systems Corp.
    533 Stevens Ave.
    Solana Bch, CA 92075

16. Eagle Signal Industrial Controls Div.
    Gulf and Western
    736 Federal St.
    Davenport, IA 52803

17. Electronic Arrays
    550 E. Middlefield Rd.
    Mountain View, CA 94043

18. Essex International
    564 Alpha Dr.
    Pittsburgh, PA 15238

19. Fabri-Tek Inc.
    5901 S. County Rd. 18
    Minn, MN 55436

20. Fairchild Semiconductor
 464 Ellis St.
 Mt. View, CA 94042

21. Fujitsu, 2-Chome 6-1
 Chiyoda-Ku Tokyo
 JAPAN

22. General Automation
 1055 S. East St.
 Anaheim, CA 92803

23. General Instrument
 600 W. John St.
 Hicksville, NY 11802

24. Harris Semiconductor
 P. O. Box 883
 Melbourne, FL 32901

25. Hitachi, 23-15 6-Chome
 Minamiohi, Shinagawa-Ku
 JAPAN

26. Intel
 3065 Bowers Ave.
 Santa Clara, CA 95051

27. International Marketing Services
 52 Garden Road
 Wellesley, MA 02181

28. Intersil Inc.
 10900 N. Tantau Ave.
 Cupertino, CA 95014

29. Martin Research
 1825 S. Halsted St.
 Chicago, IL 60608

30. Microcomputer Associates
 P. O. Box 304
 Cupertino, CA 95014

31. Microdata Corp.
 17481 Red Hill Ave.
 Irvine, CA 92705

32. Microsystems International
 Ltd.

 P. O. Box 3529 Station C
 Ottawa, CANADA KIY 4JI

33. MITS
 6328 Linn Ave.
 Albuquerque, NM 87108

34. Monolithic Memories, Inc.
 1165 E. Arques Ave.
 Sunnyvale, CA 94086

35. Monroe Calculator Co.
 550 Central Ave.
 Orange, NY 07051

36. MOS Technology
 905 Rittenhouse Rd.
 Norristown, PA 19401

37. Mostek
 1215 W. Crosby Rd.
 Carrollton, TX 75006

38. Motorola Semiconductor
 5005 E. McDowell Rd.
 Phoenix, AZ 85036

39. Multisonics
 3300 Crow Canyon Rd.
 P. O. Box 350
 San Ramon, CA 94583

40. NEC Microcomputers
 5 Militia Dr.
 Lexington, MA 02173

41. National Semiconductor
 2900 Semiconductor Dr.
 Santa Clara, CA 95051

42. Panafacom
 P. O. Box 4637
 Mountain View, CA 94040

43. Plessey Microsystems
 1674 McGau Ave.
 Santa Ana, CA 92705

44. Process Computers Systems
 5467 Hill 23 Dr.
 Flint, MI 48507

45. Pro-Log
    852 Airport Rd.
    Monterey, CA 93940

46. Raytheon Semiconductor
    350 Ellis St.
    Mountain View, CA

47. RCA
    Route 202
    Somerville, NJ 08876

48. R2E Micro Computers
    38 Garden Rd.
    Wellesley Hills, MA 02181

49. Rockwell International
    Microelectronic Device Div.
    P. O. Box 3669
    Anaheim, CA 92803

50. Scientific Micro Systems
    520 Clyde Ave.
    Mt. View, CA 94043

51. SEMI, Div. of EM&M
    3883 11. 28 Ave.
    Phoenix, AZ 85017

52. Signetics Corp.
    811 E. Arques Ave.
    Sunnyvale, CA 94086

53. Standard Logic, Inc.
    2215 S. Standard Ave.
    Santa Ana, CA 92707

54. Synertek
    3050 Coronado Dr.
    Santa Clara, CA 95051

55. Teledyne Systems
    19601 N. Nordhoff St.
    Northbridge, CA 91324

56. Texas Instruments
    P. O. Box 1443
    Houston, TX 77001

57. Three Phoenix Co.
    10632 N. 21st Ave.
    Phoenix, AZ 85029

58. Transitron
    68 Albion St.
    Wakefield, MA 01880

59. Toshiba Transistor Works
    1-Komukai
    Toshiba-Cho
    Kawasaki-Chi, JAPAN

60. Varitel Inc.
    8857 Olympic
    Beverly Hills, CA 90211

61. Warner & Swasey Electronic
    Products Division
    30300 Solon Industrial Park-
    way
    Solon, OH 44139

62. Western Digital Corp.
    3128 Red Hill
    Newport Beach, CA 95051

63. Xerox Corporation
    Dept. 15-02
    701 S. Aviation Blvd.
    El Segundo, CA 90245

64. Zilog
    10460 Bubb Road
    Cupertino, CA 95014

Appendix C
Partial List of Magazines

1. *Byte*
   Byte Publications, Inc.
   70 Main St.
   Peterborough, NH 03458

2. *Calculators / Computers*
   DYMAX
   P. O. Box 310
   Menlo Park, CA 94025

3. *Computer Music Journal*
   Peoples Computer Co.
   P. O. Box E
   Menlo Park, CA 94025

4. *Computer Notes*
   MITS Inc.
   2450 Alamo S.E.
   Albuquerque, NM 87106

5. *Creative Computing*
   Creative Computing
   P. O. Box 789-M
   Morristown, NJ 07662

6. *Digital Design*
   Benwill Publishing Corp.
   167 Corey Road
   Brookline, MA 02146

7. *Dr. Dobbs Journal*
   Peoples Computer Co.
   P. O. Box E
   Menlo Park, CA 94025

8. *EDN*
   Chaners Publishing

   270 St. Paul St.
   Denver, CO 80206

9. *Elementary Electronics*
   Davis Publications, Inc.
   P. O. Box 2530
   Greenwich, CT 06830

10. *Electronic Design*
    Hayden Publishing Co.
    50 Essex St.
    Rochelle Park, NJ 07662

11. *Electronics*
    McGraw-Hill Inc.
    McGraw Hill Bldg.
    1221 Ave. of the Americas
    New York, NY 10020

12. *Ham Radio*
    Communications Technology
    Greenville, NH 03048

13. *IEEE Computer*
    IEEE
    345 E. 47th St.
    New York, NY 10017

14. *Interface Age*
    McPheters, Wolfe & Jones
    16704 Marquardt Ave.
    Cerritos, CA 90701

15. *Kilobaud*
    Kilobaud Inc.
    Peterborough, NH 03458

16. *Microtek*
    (Now *Personal Computing*)

17. *MiniMicro Systems*
    Mini Micro Systems
    5 Kane Industrial Dr.
    Hudson, MA 01749

18. *Peoples Computer* (PCC)
    Peoples Computer Co.
    P. O. Box E
    Menlo Park, CA 94025

19. *Personal Computing*
    Benwill Publishing
    167 Corey Rd.
    Brookline, MA 02146

20. *Popular Computing*
    Popular Computing
    P. O. Box 272
    Calabasas, CA 91302

21. *Popular Electronics*
    One Park Ave.
    New York, NY 10003

22. *Radio Electronics*
    Gernsback Publications
    200 Park Ave. South
    New York, NY 10003

23. *ROM*
    ROM Publications Inc.
    Route 97
    Hampton, CT 06247

24. *SCCS Interface*
    Southern California
        Computer Society
    1415 Second St.
    Santa Monica, CA 90401

25. *73 Amateur Radio*
    73, Inc.
    Peterborough, NH 03458

Index